THE
ABSOL
MOST
CHALL
BASEBALL
QUIZ BOOK,
EVER

THE ABSOLUTELY MOST CHALLENGING

Baseball Quiz Book,

EVER

by David Nemec

COLLIER BOOKS
A Division of
Macmillan Publishing Co., Inc.
New York

For my father,
Joseph Sylvester Nemec

Copyright © 1977 by David Nemec

Macmillan Publishing Co., Inc.
866 Third Avenue, New York, N.Y. 10022
Collier Macmillan Canada, Ltd.

Library of Congress Cataloging in Publication Data

Nemec, David.
    The absolutely most challenging baseball quiz
book, ever.

    1. Baseball—United States—Miscellanea. I.
Title.
GV867.3.N45   796.357'0973   76-49934
ISBN 0-02-023190-3

First Collier Books Edition 1977

Printed in the United States of America

Contents

Introduction

For years now you've been holding court during lunch hour or at your favorite bar while you rattle off the regular infield for the 1951 Athletics or some such collection of nondescripts. A few hours here and there with your head buried in *The Baseball Encyclopedia* or *The Little Red Book of Baseball* and you've stocked your memory bank with some pretty nifty zingers: what shortstop twice made five errors in a game, who holds the record for most games caught ... that sort of thing.

Well, that's fine, but the fact is you've barely scratched the surface. You haven't earned your letter yet as a baseball expert. Not by a long shot.

Ahead of you is the ultimate challenge: the World Series of Baseball Memorabilia. You have seven games to prove yourself a champion. In each game you'll be tested on just about every aspect of the major league game since its inaugural season in 1876. You say you're dynamite on old-timers but have lost some of your edge for the game since expansion? No good. You're a specialist in the modern era? Not enough. The New York teams and maybe the Cards and the Pirates are the only ones that hold any real interest for you? Out of luck. In order to win your letter here you've got to be a true Renaissance fan, intrigued every bit as much by the 1945 Cubs as the 1927 Yankees, hip not only to Dizzy Dean and Lefty Grove but also to such forgotten hill greats as Noodles Hahn and Smokey Joe Wood. Take me at my word, if you can answer three out of ten of the questions in this book you've averaged .300 against some of the toughest pitching you could ever hope to see. My personal bet is you'll struggle to break .200. Hit .400 and I'm liable to ask for your autograph.

Some of the more difficult questions are worth a double. Those a little tougher yet go for a three-bagger. Nail my real zingers and you've earned yourself a round-tripper. And, oh yes, there are a handful of questions so extraordinary that knowing the answer to them will bring you bonus points in the form of a two-run, three-run or even a grand-slam homer! At the end of each inning you'll find the potential number of hits and also the potential number of total bases or points available to you in the inning. Bonus points too will be listed, if any. That way, if you're into some really heavy ego-tripping, you can keep a running account not only of your batting average but your slugging percentage as well. And at the end of the book you'll be able to rate your overall performance against the game's hitting stars, both past and present.

You've always secretly thought you knew a lot more about baseball than most of the so-called experts. Baby, here's your chance to prove it.

Batter up!

Game

1

They've brought you north with the big boys after a pretty fair spring. It's opening day and you're being thrown to the wolves. Last year's Cy Young winner is starting against your team and you—you've been made the designated hitter!

What better category to start with than ...

1ST INNING
Rookie

Our Cy Young winner is cocky and grooves the first pitch to you. Miss it and you're in for a long season.

1. He was voted the American League Rookie of the Year in 1954 after clouting .302 as the A's regular third-sacker. He never approached that figure again in a six-year career and wound it up as a utility infielder for the 1959 Orioles. Easy single.

2. Braves' fans groaned when the Beantowners took on two 30-year-old rookie righthanders in 1937 but by the end of the season the fans in the other seven NL cities were doing the groaning as both won 20 games. Take two but only if you get both.

3. And speaking of rookie oldsters, this 41-year-old Tiger outfielder became the oldest frosh ever to appear in over half his team's games in 1944. His last major league at-bat was in the Series a year later. Worth a triple.

4. In his first season this outfielder hit .352 for the 1899 Pirates and three years later took the NL bat crown. A leg injury in 1906 took the icing off what might have been a great career. Two-bagger.

5. Also in 1899, this Redleg portsider won 23 games and went on to post 121 victories by the time he was 25. Arm trouble short-circuited a probable Hall of Fame career a year later. A homer for this one ... to fatten you up for later.

6. What diminutive southpaw won 13 games for the Black Sox in his frosh season and two more in the tainted Series? Your clue is that two years later, after winning 19 games, he became embroiled in a vicious salary dispute with Comiskey and never won another major league game. One of the genuine victims of the reserve clause. Single.

7. What rookie Red Sox outfielder hit .302 in 1947? It was strictly a one-shot performance, for in a career that spanned ten seasons—ending with the Indians in 1956—he never again came even moderately close to .300, though he proved a good clutch hitter and showed above-average power. One.

8. The Pirates thought they had a winner when this rookie outfielder clubbed .301 and knocked in 111 runs in 1938. Two seasons later, however, they surrendered him cheaply to the Reds, and after a .230 season as a part-timer for the 1942 Dodgers he was gone. Two.

9. Another rookie wonder was this Angel backstopper who hit a solid .258 in 1962 in 155 games. He looked for all the world like their catcher for the next decade, but after his fifth consecutive sub-.240 season in 1969 he was through at 31. Bloop single.

10. In 1942 the Cards had a rookie righty who won 21 games and two more in the Series. Returning from the service in 1946, he fell to only seven wins and racked up his final two big league victories the following year after being dealt to the Braves. Was he for real in 1942? Single.

11. He started 68 games for the 1886 Baltimore Associations, winning 29, throwing three no-hitters and striking out a record 513 batters. He was only 20 then, but by the time he was 24 he'd pretty well shot his wing, winning only 11 more games in sporadic big league appearances thereafter. It's doubtful there's a man alive today who saw this fabled southpaw pitch; hence I'm offering a triple.

12. With the 1942 Red Sox he rapped .331 and followed that up with numerous other .300 seasons. He plummeted to .225, however, when dealt to the Tigers in 1952 and two years later was dropped by the Senators after a .246 showing. The added clue that he was the last man to produce 200 or more hits in his first three big league seasons makes this such an easy single you deserve to be farmed out if you don't get it.

13. Traded to the A's by the Yankees early in 1956, this outfielder stroked .314 in his debut. The next year he slumped to .245 but rapped 18 homers and fanned only 15 times. Nicknamed "The Nervous Greek," he had a flair for making contact but not often enough to much avail, it seemed, for he was gone by 1959. Take two.

14. After a brief trial in 1941, this Bengal rook came up to stay with a bang two years later, leading the AL in hits and doubles while stroking a deft .316. Drafted in midseason the following year, he returned in 1946 minus some vital part—more mental than physical, his managers contended—and managed to hang on till the early '50s, though he never lived up to the super-star status that had been predicted for him as a rookie. Infield scratch.

15. In 1901 this Tiger rook won 23 games and set an all-time record for complete games by a rookie. The following year he slipped to seven wins, a total he duplicated with the Pirates in 1904, his final year. Little else is known about this rookie wonderman, who died in 1913. I'll ante up a homer for this one.

Potential Hits: 15
Potential Points: 29
Bonus Points: 0

(Answers on Page 136)

You've got an inning under your belt now. Probably you're hitting well over .300.

The fun, however, is just beginning. You went ape on rookies; now let's try you on the opposite end of the spectrum.

2ND INNING
Ole Man River

Each of the following questions deals with a player who had his first real big league shot at age 30 or older. Some of these joint-creakers had enough left to go on to great careers, and one or two even made the Hall of Fame. But all had one thing in common: they proved that in spite of their belated opportunity they belonged.

1. This flame-thrower didn't win his first big league game till he was 31, but before he was through he racked up 196 more. In his only Series appearance—with the 1934 Cards—he was then 43. For shame if you don't collect an easy bingle on this dazzler.

2. In 1927 he received his first genuine chance at 30 and went on to register four consecutive .300 seasons for the Braves. A skilled outfielder and baserunner, he had little power despite his formidable name. His son, an artist, specializes in painting old baseball scenarios, many depicting his father in action. Homer.

3. A rookie at 33 with the 1953 White Sox, he won 16 for them the following year and was in double figures as late as 1957 when he also threw a no-hitter. Worth two.

4. Though he didn't play his first bigtop game till he was 33, he made up for lost time by posting a lifetime .281 average and gave Cleveland some outstanding backstopping in the AL's maiden season. Two-run homer.

5. Already 32 when the Dodgers acquired him in 1924 after a short earlier trial with the Giants, he rattled off four solid .300 seasons and nearly 900 career hits for the Dodgers and Braves. A weak arm made him something of an outfield liability. With that and the added clue that he once held the NL record for consecutive games played, you should get two.

6. Arriving on the scene at 36 with the 1937 A's, he hit .374 the following season as their backup to Hayes. In an abbreviated four-year career he hit .290, giving ample cause to believe he could have done it all if given the chance earlier. I shouldn't do it, but your clue for a triple is that he later coached for Connie.

7. Age 34 when the NL was formed, he'd already had a long professional career. This first-sacker still had enough left, however, to play 11 more seasons and post a lifetime .300 average. Instrumental in breaking the winning streak of the 1869 Red Stockings. Homer.

8. As a 32-year-old rook for the 1946 Browns he won only three games and gave no intimation that he had the stuff to win 20 three years later and lead the AL in winning percentage. Finished out a 12-year career with the 1957 Pale Hose. Single.

9. An 18-game winner as a 31-year-old rookie with the 1924 Pirates and their leading hurler in the fall classic the following season, he was a big winner as late as 1930 when he chalked up a league-leading 20 victories. Had 147 triumphs lifetime, all with the Pirates, and a .627 winning percentage. So unheralded is this old chucker that I feel safe in giving you a triple for him.

A ripe 41 when he reached the majors, he took the mound 62 times for the 1962 Pirates at age 43. (Question 10)

10. A ripe 41 when he reached the majors, he took the mound 62 times for the 1962 Pirates at age 43 and was 5 −1. Two-bagger.

11. After an abortive trial four years earlier with the Tigers, this 30-year-old flychaser was given a reprieve by the Reds in 1922 and showed his gratitude by rapping .340. As a further display that he'd belonged in big league company all along, he hit .349 for the 1925 Phils. A lifetime .303 hitter with good power, he played in his only series with the 1928 Cards. Another deuce.

12. Cast off by the 1919 Indians after a .375 season as a utility man, he emerged from retirement three years later with the Red Sox. Given his first chance to play regularly at 31, he went on to hit over .300 in each of the next six seasons and was the hitting star of the 1925 Series with three homers and a .400 average. Lifetime a .317 thumper, he finished with the 1928 Dodgers. A hard single.

13. A one-game trial in 1937 was his only smell of big league action until the Senators employed him as a wartime fill-in in 1944. His skills seemed to sharpen under the challenge, and by the late '40s he was strong enough to take the A's catching job away from a fading Rosar. In 1950, at age 38, he had perhaps his finest year, stroking a neat .282. Double.

14. Tried and found wanting by the Senators in the mid-'20s, he bobbed up at 31 with the 1930 Cards and hit an unbelievable .374 in 92 games. His glove work was so awful, however, that the Cards unloaded him anyway. Two years later, given a last glance by the Browns, he lasted fewer than 20 games. Homer for this flychaser.

15. Already 30 when the Giants finally gave him a look in 1930 and 33 before he arrived to stay with the 1933 White Sox, he pitched in 430 games despite a late start, all but 40 in relief, and totaled 76 career wins. Top years were with the Indians and Red Sox, and for nearly a decade he gave Murphy a battle for the title of the AL's top fireman. A double to give you a running start for the next inning.

Potential Hits: 15
Potential Points: 37
Bonus Points: 1

(Answers on Page 136)

Still hitting .300?

In that case, I'd better get down to serious business in this next inning and bring on my number one ...

3RD INNING
Hose

1. The most wins by an NL pitcher since Dean's 30 in 1934 was _____ by _____ in _____ . One base for each correct answer.

2. The AL's top winner in 1942 as a sophomore, this Texan later fell prey to arm trouble but still managed to post 96 career wins and a lifetime .640 winning percentage, all for the same club. Two.

3. This NL ace racked up 82 wins in a brief four-year career from 1898 to 1902 (he sat out the 1901 season). In his final year, with the Dodgers, he won 15 and finished 27 of 30 starts; yet he vanished from the scene at only 28. Same name as a later-day Dodger reliever. Homer.

4. After eight indifferent seasons as a combination starter-reliever, this Cub righty went almost exclusively to the bullpen in 1958 and lasted ten more seasons with seven different teams. In two Series and the AL leader in saves with the Indians in 1960, he had a .596 winning percentage as a reliever but only .350 as a starter. Single.

5. The Red Sox got him from the Browns in 1948 for pennant insurance, and in truth he did a fine job for them, winning 18 and leading the AL in winning percentage. After 1948, however, he won only ten games and was gone by 1951. One for this handsome righty.

6. Between 1937—43 he posted an incredible 37-9 record for the Cards. His top year was 1941 when he was 10—0. Returning from the service in 1946, he lost two games in relief and was unloaded. Still he compiled an almost unreal .771 winning percentage lifetime. Cinch triple for '40s fans.

7. Who was the only hurler since 1900 to have seasons in which he won 25 or more games in both leagues? Even with the clue that it ain't Cy Young, it's still worth two.

8. As a rookie he started six games for the 1907 Highlanders and pitched three shutouts. In his only relief appearance he went five scoreless innings. Little biographical info is known about him and less is known about why the Highlanders let him get away after such a fantastic beginning. This could be your first grandslam.

9. From 1901 through 1919, four Hall of Fame hurlers—Young, Walsh, Waddell and Johnson—dominated the AL in strikeouts. Only once, in 1909, did an outsider slip through to lead the league in K's. For a three-bagger, who was this White Sox upstart?

10. Despite a 34−15 record through 1959 as a reliever, this Red Sox righty was made almost exclusively into a starter in 1960 and labored on for four more seasons as a sub-.500 pitcher. In 1956 he was perhaps the AL's top fireman, finishing 11−2 in relief; overall he was 84−75, all for the Sox. A tough leg hit.

11. Which of the following Hall of Famers never pitched in the majors: Cobb, Williams, DiMaggio, Anson, Hornsby, Delahanty, Speaker, Goslin and Wagner? One base for each correct *never*; one base deducted for any who did pitch incorrectly identified as a *never*.

12. He won his 200th game in 1934 in a Yankee uniform, but he was paid for most of his career to beat the Bombers, a feat he accomplished with pretty good success. The AL's workhorse from 1922−26, he twice led in wins and complete games and three times in starts. He had the good fortune for most of his career to pitch in his hometown and in his only Series pitched three shutout innings against the Dodgers. Single.

13. The name of the last man to have the distinction of pitching on Yankee, Dodger and Giant pennant winners when all three were still in New York is only worth one.

14. Who was the only pitcher except McGinnity and Flaherty to win 20 while dividing the season between the two leagues? Your clue is he was also the last pitcher to figure in four decisions in the same World Series; both feats were accomplished in the same year. Should be a simple one.

Potential Hits: 14
Potential Points: 31
Bonus Points: 3

(Answers on Page 136)

4TH INNING
Not with a Whimper but with a Bang

Each of the players here, unlike the majority of major leaguers who wind down gradually and eventually fade away to a whisper, had a final season worth remembering. With very few exceptions, and these always noted, none of the players in this category ever appeared in a big league boxscore again after his finale.

1. This outfielder jumped from the Cubs to the AL in 1900 when it was still a minor league and won the batting title. In 1901 he hit .320 with the Senators and hung 'em up. A ringing double.

2. In 1942 this big righthander won 14 and pitched in nearly 250 innings for the Browns. He finished with 130 wins at 32, though your old man who saw him pitch will swear he was much older. One.

3. This former mound ace became an outfielder when his wing went and packed it in in order to accept the Yale coaching job after hitting .297 with 92 RBIs for the 1922 Indians. Single.

4. The Yankees acquired this first-sacker from the Braves prior to the 1942 season and he gave them a .284 bat and some outstanding Series play before calling it quits. Lifetime .292, his finest all-around season was his first—with the 1936 Dodgers. One.

5. Out of nowhere he hit .302 for the 1945 White Sox and narrowly missed the bat crown. His best previous performance had been .254 as a part-time Pirate flychaser in 1937. Two for this wartime marvel.

6. Back in the majors in 1949 after an unsuccessful trial with the 1946 Giants, he pounded 24 homers for the Browns, third best in the AL. Nevertheless this lefty first-sacker was found deficient overall and not retained. Two more.

7. This 23-year-old outfielder with the unlikely nickname of "Pop" had a sturdy .279 season for the 1901 Senators after jumping from the Freedman-oppressed Giants. He vanished after that, taking with him a .281 lifetime average and seemingly rosy future in the game. You'll earn this three-run-homer.

8. The Tigers picked up this slick Brownie first-sacker in 1936, and he hit a solid .283 after taking over for the injured Greenberg. Next season, with Greenberg healthy again, he was demoted to Toledo, finished at only 29 after six seasons as a regular. I'd like to give more, but two is all it's worth.

9. After rapping .316 for the 1945 Cardinals, he wasn't thought worthy of being invited back for 1946 when their prewar gardeners came trooping home. Gift homer.

10. There was a great deal of furor a few years back when Pappas won 200 games without ever having a 20-win season; but this old NL portsider won 197, including 15 in his finale with the 1942 Dodgers, without ever entering the charmed 20-game circle. One.

11. The 1948 Indians were carried to the pennant by Bearden, Lemon and Feller, but equally important perhaps was the contribution of a 41-year-old reliever who posted a league-leading 17 saves and a 2.90 ERA. For a two-bagger, who was he?

12. A star with the fabled Red Stockings, he was still in his prime in 1879 when he called it quits at 29 after a .297 season as a player-manager for the not so successful Cincinnati franchise in the NL. Sounds hard but it's really only worth a single.

13. He won 223 games between 1912 and 1926, all for the same team. In his finale he topped the AL with 11 relief wins. Like so many greats, he never pitched in a Series; nor did he ever lead the league in a major pitching stat despite three 20-game seasons. Should be a fairly easy double.

Potential Hits: 13
Potential Points: 25
Bonus Points: 2

(Answers on Page 136)

Okay, by now you're hip to my thing. I'll give you a couple of off-speed tosses in the form of a weird career, a freak season, and then flip you my blue darter once I've got you set up.

You know what I'm doing to you, but what are you doing in return? You've got four innings under your belt now; let's take a moment out to see how well you're doing. If you've rapped 20 hits or better thus far, no two ways about it, you've got my number. If you're somewhere between 13 and 19, we're good competition for each other. Much less than 13? Well, no doubt you feel I ought to build your confidence a little by throwing a few easy ones your way. But somehow, by now, you must know I'm not going to do that.

Instead I'm going to feed you ...

5TH INNING
The Unrewarded

My personal favorite category and one you can expect to see a lot of.

1. He completed an 18-year career with the 1905 Red Sox. For over a decade he was one of the top catchers in the majors for a string of lackluster teams and a deadly pinch-hitter, probably the first to make an art of it. Top years were with Washington, though in 1891 with Boston he led the old Association in homers and RBIs. Take two.

2. After five solid seasons in the NL, this Cardinal outfielder jumped to the Brooklyn Feds in 1914 where he hit .348 and led the league in slugging percentage. The first of many Fed stars we're going to encounter whom the majors refused to take back, he never played in a big league uniform again after the Feds folded. Three.

3. In a 21-year career he compiled 2644 hits. The AL's premier third-sacker as late as 1906 after starting his career as a catcher with the old Louisville Association team in 1887, this Czech star, like the rest of his teammates, was pretty well stymied by Mathewson in his only Series. Single.

4. A 15-year vet, this AL outfielder called it quits after the

1945 season. He'd amassed over 2000 hits and nearly 300 homers without ever leading the AL in a major offensive category or playing in a Series. His finest years were with the dismal Athletic teams of the middle '30s. Single.

5. Twice a NL batting title winner, long a steady .300 hitter and a fine defensive outfielder, he retired after the 1891 season. In a 20-year career he had over 2000 hits and the distinction of playing for both the first NL pennant winner and the fabled Providence teams of the early '80s. Cinch two for oldies fans.

6. Injuries kept this catcher from enjoying the genuine stardom his talent should have brought him. In his peak year, playing in a park that was anathema to his power alley in left-center, he still hit 35 homers and knocked in 122 runs. Only Johnny Bench has had a better power year since, and no catcher ever, excepting perhaps Berra, has matched his combination of longevity and the long ball. The man with the big hitch in his swing, he played for every NL team except the Phils and Dodgers between 1940–57. Single.

7. The first genuine Jewish star, he, along with countless other early greats, was a victim of the infamous NL blacklist and was dropped by Providence after the 1878 season while still in his prime. Stretch this into a triple.

8. He hurled for every AL team except the Tigers and A's between 1914–35 and is the only player who was a teammate of both Lajoie and Whitlow Wyatt. Won 229 games and was in four Series. One base.

9. Age 27 the year he appeared in his first major league boxscore and 39 the year he appeared in his last, he posted 195 career wins despite his relatively late start, all with the same club. A four-time 20-game winner between 1899–1906, his finest season was 1903 when he was 25–7 before losing two games in the Series. Two-bagger.

10. At 30 he was one of the AL's standout outfielders with a lifetime .320 average and 1200 hits despite losing three years to the service. A crippling back injury kept him out all of 1949, however, and he never really made it back. Finished as a pinch-swinger for the 1953 Indians. A line single, in the fashion of this Irish-Lithuanian.

11. What Cleveland-born shortstop played all of his career except his final season in his hometown after breaking in with the 1887 Association team and moving to the Spiders in 1889 where he remained until ten years later when he was made part of the mass transfer of Spider stars to St. Louis? There are several shortstops in the Hall of Fame with less going for them than his .303 average with over 2000 hits, but his name today is virtually unknown, even in Cleveland. In standing with a triple.

12. A left-handed-hitting catcher with a lifetime .300 average over seven seasons of work disappeared mysteriously from the big league scene at only 29 after two solid seasons with the Federal League Packers. An All-Star by most standards with the 1910 Indians and the 1914 Packers, he was the first in the AL to compile 30 lifetime pinch-hits. You can end this inning with a two-run homer.

Potential Hits: 12
Potential Points: 24
Bonus Points: 1

(*Answers on Page 136*)

Take a moment out to calculate your up-to-date stats.
Unless you're flirting with the .300 mark, I'm afraid about the best you can hope for from here on in is a moment or two as an ...

---

6 TH INNING
Unlikely Hero

1. In his last full season of play this chunky White Sox outfielder hit four home runs in an extra-inning game. Single.

2. In 1925, his only year as a regular, this Tiger outfielder hit .370. Though he never again came even remotely close to a .300 season, the cushion provided by his 1925 performance gave him a lifetime .308 average. A triple, and you deserve it.

3. For one year—1959—he could do no wrong, slamming 20 homers and hitting at a .363 clip. His lifetime average over 15 seasons was approximately 100 points lower, though he was at times a dangerous pinch-hitter. Finished with the 1970 Brewers. One.

4. He hit a torrid .403 for the 1957 Braves as a part-time outfielder with many key hits down the stretch drive. The following year he slumped to .211 and faded summarily. Scratch hit.

5. After shutting out Feller and the Indians to clinch the 1940 flag for the Tigers, he never won another big league game, having won only two previously. Two-bagger.

6. Although not quite good enough to do more than platoon with Lee Handley at third for the 1940 Pirates, he nevertheless got in just enough games to win the bat title that year. One base.

7. The Braves acquired this former A's utility man to play first in 1925 and were jubilant when he hit .340 and had 200 hits. The following season he dropped to .270, reverting to form, and after two more years as a part-timer he slipped quietly from view. Three.

8. After four years as a journeyman infielder, this Brave second-sacker suddenly blossomed in 1911 and 1912, hitting .314 and .344 respectively. Two years later he was down to .218 after being dealt to the Cubs for Evers and was released at only 28. Two.

9. He led the NL in RBIs with 130 in 1965 and seemed finally to be coming into his own. Two years later he hit .224 and the following year dropped to .208 and 33 RBIs. Yet in 1976, at age 38, he was still in the game, parlaying that 1965 season for more than it was worth, it would seem, for he had few good ones afterward. Single.

10. After several mediocre years with the Indians, the last in 1909, he dropped out of the majors until 1915 when the Pirates acquired him from the minors at 32. For the next two seasons he was one of the NL's standout outfielders, ranking high among bat leaders both years, and may well have gone on for several more seasons had he not suffered a broken leg in 1917. You rate a triple.

11. After winning the AL bat crown in 1932, he slipped badly the following year after being burned by a careless trainer. Nevertheless, this big first-sacker managed to hit well over .300 in four of his five big league seasons, including .349 as a rook for the 1929 Tigers. Forgotten today, he had a career .331 and twice knocked in over 130 runs. Double.

12. A weak stick caused the A's and Red Sox to give up on this shortstop. Picked up by the Highlanders, he went bananas in 1910, rapping .312 and briefly replacing Barry as the league's top shortstop. He made an effort to hold his ground in 1911 but dropped quickly back into the pack after that and was gone by 1913 with a career .239. Two-run homer.

13. Runner-up for the AL bat crown in 1968 with a .290 average, he picked the league's poorest hitting season to have one of his best. Two.

> *Potential Hits: 13*
> *Potential Points: 26*
> *Bonus Points: 1*
>
> *(Answers on Page 137)*

7TH INNING
Outstanding Offenders

An easy inning and a chance for you to fatten up.

1. He holds the record for the most seasons having 600 or more at-bats, all with the same team and all in a row. Single.

2. Who is the only man ever to compile more than 1500 career walks and fewer than 2000 hits? Another single.

3. Through the 1976 season there were five men in history who had won two or more bat titles while possessing less than a .300 lifetime average. A triple for all five; two for four; no credit for less.

4. A single for the player who had the highest average in his first season as a regular (over 400 at-bats).

5. Name the first NL'er to amass over 50 career pinch-hits and I'll give you a triple.

6. Kauff was known as the Cobb of the Federal League. Who qualifies as the Ruth? A homer for this slugger.

7. Easy single for the Union Association bat leader in its only year of existence.

8. After five successive seasons in which he hit .353 or better, he slipped to .275 in 1898 and was gone a year later. Still he stayed long enough to compile over 1000 hits and a lifetime .339 average, mostly for the Pirates. Two-run homer.

The only man ever to compile more than 1500 career walks and fewer than 2000 hits. (Question 2)

9. When Mattie Alou made 698 plate appearances in 1970, he broke a 34-year-old record held by this former Pirate outfielder. Two.

10. Who was the last catcher to win a batting title? One.

11. The name of the only man to win NL bat crowns both before and after 1900 will bring you a two-bagger.

12. The complete lead-off man, he led the NL in walks seven times between 1899 and 1907 while averaging better than .300 and scoring over 100 runs per season. This old Phillie outfielder died in 1959 at 85, forgotten by all but a special few. For a homer, are you one who remembers?

13. The Babe broke this old first-sacker's lifetime home run record when he hit his 137th in 1921. Worth a homer a couple of years ago, but now, with all the Aaron hoopla, it's too shopworn to go for more than a double.

14. In 1954 this Phillie catcher hit .368 but failed by a few dozen at-bats to qualify for the bat title. He never approached that figure again, although as late as 1966 he hit .313 as a spot player and pinch-hitter deluxe. A single. See, didn't I tell you you'd fatten up?

Potential Hits: 14
Potential Points: 27
Bonus Points: 1

(Answers on Page 137)

You're doing so well they're taking you out of the designated hitter's spot and putting you in the regular lineup.

Let's hope in comparing you to the man you replaced we'll be able to say at the end of the season that the substitution was a case of ...

8TH INNING
Wine for Water

1. Who preceded Ruth as the Yankees' regular right-fielder? This one is so well known by now it's only worth a single.

2. The man Cobb replaced as the Tigers' regular center-fielder. Two.

3. The Yankee first-sacker prior to Gehrig. Easy single.

4. The Yankee first-sacker who replaced Gehrig. Another one.

5. He was replaced by Ted Williams. (Hint: Williams played rightfield as a rookie. Double hint: The man he replaced hit .340 the previous year.) Two-bagger.

6. He replaced Appling as the White Sox shortstop. (Hint: Appling moved to third in 1948.) Cheap double.

7. DiMaggio replaced him as the Yankees' regular center-fielder. (Hint: DiMag played left primarily as a rookie.) Two.

8. A broken ankle suffered by this player in a pre-season game gave Aaron the Braves' left-field slot in 1954. Single.

9. The same man who was replaced by Aaron was replaced by another great at a different outfield position for a different team three years earlier. Single for that great.

10. He replaced Kiner as the Pirate left-fielder in 1953 and hit 30 homers in his own right. One base.

11. Richie Ashburn hit .333 as a rookie but still fell some 30 points short of the man he replaced. Who was that man, for a single?

Potential Hits: 11
Potential Points: 15
Bonus Points: 0

(Answers on Page 137)

9TH INNING
Fall Classic

A bit early in the year for the World Series, you might say, but I like to try my competition early.

1. Who was the first pitcher to win three games in a Series? Two.

2. Who was the leading hitter of the first Series and also hit the first Series homer? Three.

3. Who was the only pitcher to lose three games in a Series? Two.

4. What team won a Series with a staff ERA of 7.11? Two.

5. In 1959, his only Series, he won two games, saved two others, and hit .500. Single.

6. Who was the first to hit two homers in a Series game? Two.

7. Who is the only player ever to compile as many career Series hits as he did career regular-season hits? I'll demand a saliva test if you get it but if you do it's a grand slam all the way.

8. What was the worst team batting average, within five points, in a Series? What team? What year? Must get all three for a single.

9. What team lost a Series despite posting a team batting average of .338? Single.

10. Hodges went 0 for 21 in the 1952 Series, a record for Series ineptness. It was broken when this infielder went 0 for 22 in a more recent Series. Homer.

11. His passed ball on a third strike allowed the Cubs to tie the 1907 Series opener in the 9th inning. His team went on to lose in four straight. Everybody remembers Mickey Owen, but it's worth a two-run homer if you remember this early-day goat.

Potential Hits: 11
Potential Points: 26
Bonus Points: 4

(Answers on Page 137)

Game

2

You ought to be a little cocky now, having done so well in the last game. However, the pitching this time around gets a bit stiffer, and after a look at some of the tosses I'm going to give you, you couldn't be blamed if you cried ...

1ST INNING
Don't Fence Me In

Sure, you know all about Ruth, Aaron and Maris, but how about some of these other home run kings?

1. Who is the only player since the advent of the lively ball to win a homer crown while striking out less than ten times? Two.

2. What NL'er hit only one round-tripper prior to winning the homer crown and never hit another one afterward. Homer.

3. What other NL'er never hit another homer after earning a co-holder's share of the crown in 1907? Take four.

4. What modern player (since 1900) was once a co-holder of the home run crown in the NL despite having fewer than 220 official at-bats? Single.

5. A single for the name of the last AL'er to hit four homers in a game of regulation length.

6. In 1919 when Ruth hit an "incredible" 29 homers to break all then-existing records, what Yankee was one of the three AL'ers who tied for the runner-up spot with ten? One.

7. Who was the first NL'er to hit 40 homers in a season? Two.

8. In 1927 Ruth's 60 homers was greater than the total achieved by how many of the other seven AL teams? Two.

9. Who is the only man to register 40 homers and fewer than 100 RBIs in the same season? One.

Potential Hits: 9
Potential Points: 18
Bonus Points: 0

(Answers on Page 137)

2ND INNING
Monickers

You've been working hard and deserve an easy inning. Who were known by the following nicknames?

1. Lady. Take two.
2. Piano Legs. And two more.
3. Line Drive. Sorry, only one.
4. Shucks. One.
5. Egyptian. Four biggies.
6. Pidge. Three.
7. Sport. Two.
8. Rudy the Red Hot Rapper. One.
9. Spook. One.
10. Nixey. Two.
11. Chicken. (Credit for a single for either of two.)
12. Corky. One.
13. Stubby. One
14. Coot. One.

Potential Hits: 14
Potential Points: 23
Bonus Points: 0

(Answers on Page 138)

3RD INNING
Metomania

No other major league team has ever captured the public imagination quite so quickly or so incisively as the Mets. Within two years of their creation they were already a legend. No one, least of all me, believes for a minute that you've forgotten Rod Kanehl or Jay Hook or Marvelous Marv, but how about these other lovables?

1. This slick-fielding rookie was an early-season sensation

in 1963 as he gave the Met fans their first taste of major league shortstopping. A weak stick did him in, however—.195 lifetime in 135 games—and when McMillan was obtained early the following season he was sent out and never returned. Triple.

2. In their first year of existence the Mets had four throwers who lost 17 or more games. Three of them were Craig, Hook and Jackson. What about the fourth? Homer.

3. Who was the first Met hitter to lead the National League in a major offensive category? Deuce.

4. The Mets' top rookie winner was _____ who won _____ in _____. The name's worth a single. Add two more for the victory total and an additional base for the year.

5. 1966 was a watershed year as the Mets came up with two hurlers who not only won in double figures but, more incredibly, had winning records! A triple awaits you, but only if you get both.

6. Third base has always been the Mets' bane. In their 14-year existence only twice have they had the same man play the position regularly two years in a row. For a double name both these repeat regulars.

7. When the Angels demanded somebody in addition to Ryan before they would part with Fregosi, the Mets threw in this outfielder, who proved himself perhaps the Angels' steadiest all-around player the next four years. One.

8. The 1964 Mets for the first time in their short life had a .300 hitting regular. More than that, they had two! For a double, who were these early Met strokers?

9. Met fans have been trying for years to block this memory out, but for everyone else it should be an easy single. What present-day American League star left Shea in the deal for Joe Foy?

10. Now of course if I ask you who was the first Met to knock in over 100 runs in a season, you'll knock it back through my legs for a single.

Potential Hits: 10
Potential Points: 23
Bonus Points: 0

(Answers on Page 138)

4TH INNING
Rookie

1. As a frosh gardener with the 1930 Cards he hit an incredible .373. Over the next six years he leveled off considerably but was still a fair enough sticker and a solid all-around performer for four NL teams. Two bases.

2. The Pirates assumed they had the perfect hot corner man to play beside Wagner when this St. Louis–born rook hit .355 in 1899 and led the NL in triples. After slipping to .264 in 1900, however, he jumped to the Orioles, who converted him to second. He spent the rest of his 11-year career in the AL as a steady but never again spectacular player and died in St. Pete at 88. Three.

3. Under the rules then in existence he qualified for the AL bat title as a rookie in 1938. However, the league wisely awarded the crown elsewhere as he had only 263 official at-bats. To show his rookie outing was no fluke he posted a .324 mark as late as 1947. In a service-abbreviated career he hit .311 over nine seasons, all unfortunately for weak clubs. Single.

4. Awarded Rookie-of-the-Year honors in 1950 after he hit .322 and knocked in a league-leading 144 runs, this first-sacker built that one season into a 13-year career as a mediocre slugger with five clubs, ending with the Orioles in the early '60s. One.

5. This Red Sox outfielder hit .347 in 1902 and followed it up with a .331 soph season. Traded in 1904 despite the vigorous protests of Sox fans, he spent the remainder of his ten-year career on a long downhill ride. With the Hitless Wonders, for example, he fit right in, stroking a palid .221. Double.

6. After opening with a solid .289 debut at second for the 1901 Indians, he became expendable when they acquired Lajoie the following year and was shipped to Detroit. After a half-season with the Bengals, he moved on to the Reds, slapping .301 between the two teams. Oddly, despite his good marks both at bat and in the field, he was dropped at age 24 and never played in the majors again. Two-run homer.

7. Seemingly comfortably ensconced for a few years at least as the Browns' regular third-baseman after rapping 15 homers and stroking .269 in 1952, he produced a .213 encore and spent the next three seasons winding down in utility roles, the last with the 1956 Reds. Fluke triple.

8. He was one of the NL's early sluggers, starting in 1904 when he led in homers and triples as a rookie. After four solid seasons, his stroke disappeared suddenly and he bowed out in 1910 as the Dodgers' player-manager. Line single.

9. A combination first-sacker and outfielder with the Pirates in 1953, he hit .283. The following year (incredibly, considering the caliber of Pirate teams in the early '50s) he was shipped out. Returning in 1957 from two years in the service, he showed little with the Bucs and was sent to the Cubs, where he showed less. Ultimately, then, the Pirates' judgment would seem vindicated, but still one wonders. Tough double.

10. Although he was 17−4 for the 1944 Cards mostly in starting roles, this bulky hurler made his rep in relief. In 1949, for example, he was 10−3 and led the NL in saves and games pitched. He finished with the 1953 Indians after coming to them the year before. One.

11. The NL's ERA leader for the 1951 Braves, he returned in 1954 after two years in the service but couldn't seem to pick up where he'd left off and disappeared till the early '60s, when he resurfaced briefly as a reliever with the Red Sox. Just one.

12. Few rooks have received as much ballyhoo as that which attended the arrival of this Texan in 1947. No one could decide at first whether he belonged on the mound or in the outfield. Six years later the decision was finally made that he didn't belong at all. In that time he hit .238 and won 29 games, scarcely a whisper of the bang he was supposed to make. Single.

13. A 14-game winner in 269 innings as a rook with the 1913 Reds, he leaped to the Feds the following year. Despite winning 18 games for the 1915 Packers, he—like so many Fed stars—was not invited back to the bigtop. A two-run homer if you recall this hard-throwing righty.

14. The Red Sox tried a lot of rookies in the early '50s, but none did better in their debut than this smooth center-fielder who rapped .283 in 1953. A year later he went to Washington as part of the Jensen "steal" and was dropped after a .219 season in 1955. Despite his size, he showed little power, even in inviting Fenway. Two bases.

15. At 18 he was burning up the NL for the 1957 Cards when arm trouble decked him. He never recovered and was through at 19, though his older brother, who had scarcely a day of arm miseries, was still around some 18 years later. A single, but only if you name both of these pitching sibs.

Potential Hits: 15
Potential Points: 29
Bonus Points: 2

(Answers on Page 138)

5TH INNING
The Unrewarded

1. This old-timer was 29 the year the NL was formed, but he had enough left to amass over 1600 hits and a .303 average. After playing with back-to-back pennant winners his first two seasons, he suffered nearly ten years of drab outfits before landing with the Wolverines in the late '80s. Usually a third-sacker, he had a brother who was the Association's top pitcher in its early years. Two, but only if you name both of these forgotten sib stars.

2. Already 30 before he was finally given the chance to play regularly, for the next ten seasons he was one of the AL's top sluggers and nearly led his team to a pennant in 1922, the year he broke Ruth's home run reign. A severe beaning slowed him in 1925, but four years later he still had enough left to hit .345 for the Red Sox as a part-time outfielder. Single.

3. One of the rarest of all birds, a right-handed batsman and a left-handed thrower, this old-timer patrolled the outfield for seven different teams between 1890 and 1907, with a peak of .327 for the 1903 Cardinals and a low the following year of .229 for the Senators. He compiled over 2200 hits and had a pitching brother who also starred in both

leagues. Two, but again only if you name both of these unsung sibs.

4. A perennial holdout, he lost three seasons in his prime due to salary disputes and another after suffering a broken leg. Just so, in a vastly shortened career he batted .333 and four times was a runner-up for league bat titles. Starting in 1899, he posted .300 seasons with six different teams in both leagues. One for the man McGraw called one of the best pure hitters he ever saw.

5. A bad back cut short this second-baseman's career while he was still at his peak. In 14 seasons, all with the same club, he posted over 2000 hits and 1200 RBIs. A frequent All-Star, he led the AL in slugging in 1944. Your guess why he's never merited even moderate Hall of Fame attention. One.

6. He achieved six successive .300 seasons for the Reds in the '20s and had a lifetime .310 average. One of the few catchers ever to win a batting crown, he ended his career as Dickey's backup. Perhaps the easiest double you'll ever get.

7. This Indian slugger received a rap for being a poor clutch performer after hitting a dismal .219 for the contending Indians in 1940. Eight years later, however, he hit 100 points higher for a pennant winner before being deprived of his only chance to play in a Series by an ill-fated late-season slide. One.

8. With seven clubs between 1923 and 1934, this big first-sacker had a lifetime .308 average, including a high of .354 for the 1929 Dodgers. Never much of a long-ball threat despite his size, he was nevertheless a skilled base thief. A pinch-hitter in his only Series appearance with the 1923 Yankees, he made the Dodgers the benefactors of his most productive seasons. Take four.

9. This pinch-hitter extraordinaire got his chance at a regular job after years as Bill Terry's understudy when he was dealt to the Dodgers in 1933. After three good years with them, he returned to the Giants in 1936 and played regularly for them all season—only to be relegated once more to a pinch-hit role in favor of his old nemesis Terry, who after acting as his former caddy's caddy, assumed control once more in the Series. Generous deuce.

10. Four times the NL's RBI leader, twice the slugging leader, once the batting leader, this old outfielder also stands twelfth on the all-time base-stealing list. He played 16 years, but it wasn't till his final bow—in 1919—that he appeared in a Series. A somewhat rowdy performer, and an epileptic, he was banned prior to the 1920 season. Sounds easy, but you'll earn this two.

11. He labored nearly his entire career with the lowly Browns but nonetheless was one of the AL's most consistently effective hurlers between 1928–34. Given a career with the Yanks or Cards of that period, he could feasibly have doubled his 104 career victory total. He never broke .500 until 1936 when he was with the Indians—one of the few seasons he played on a team that broke .500! Three.

12. He lost four seasons and a potential Hall of Fame career to the service after hitting .359 in 1941. Returning late in 1945, he had little left and packed it in after an awful .216 season in 1947. An All-Star at both third and short, he played his entire 12-year career with one team—a perennial AL doormat—and had a lifetime .314 average. Hard enough for a double.

Potential Hits: 12
Potential Points: 23
Bonus Points: 0

(Answers on Page 138)

6TH INNING
A Man for Another Season

A new category and one the all-around sports fan should use to build a nice cushion.

1. Who was the only Heisman Trophy winner to play in the majors? One.

2. One base for each pro football Hall of Famer you can name who also played big league baseball. No credit for fewer than three.

3. He combined the best of two worlds, playing the outfield for the 1948 Browns and the backfield for the AAC Yankees that autumn. Three, if you go hard all the way.

4. This Duke backfield great might have done better if he'd stuck to the gridiron for his professional days, for he

The 1965–66 Detroit Pistons basketball team had two forwards who pitched in the majors. (Question 9)

hit only .270 lifetime as a ballplayer and most of that was accomplished as a wartime Redleg outfielder. Two for the Blue Devils' pride.

5. A star Colorado back in the early '50s forsook football for baseball with unhappy results, as he averaged only .225 over an eight-year career as an outfielder with the Indians and Red Sox. Single.

6. What present-day pro golfer once led the AL in RBIs? Single.

7. The father of a present-day NFL coach, he hit .313 for the 1925 Red Sox in his only year as a regular and later managed the Phils. Shouldn't be too hard to get two on this.

8. The Boston College football team in the early '50s had two ill-fated stars who went on to play in the majors. One, a Red Sox first-sacker, died of pneumonia complications in 1955; the second, an Oriole catcher, was killed in a 1956 plane crash. Must get both for a homer.

9. The 1965–66 Detroit Pistons had two forwards who pitched in the majors. For a single, name both.

10. A college hardcourt whiz at Baldwin Wallace, he looked like a comer for a time with the Indians in the early '60s. The service, however, interrupted a promising mound career. Believe a homer.

11. Another who might have done better to stick to the gridiron was this Florida U. glamour boy who tried for years to make it as a big league catcher and concluded seven seasons of mediocrity with the A's in 1963. Single.

12. For a homer name the onetime NFL fullback who got a brief shot at the A's catching job in 1942 and rapped .389 in 16 games. After the war, he returned to football for the balance of his professional career, mostly spent as a backup.

13. Baylor's greatest quarterback ever, he turned his back on pro football to try his hand on the diamond as a catcher but never progressed so far as to play in a single big league game. Two.

Potential Hits: 13
Potential Points: 26
Bonus Points: 1

(Answers on Page 139)

7TH INNING
Not with a Whimper but with a Bang

1. This bespectacled third-sacker carried a career-long rap as a bad fielder, but there was nothing wrong with his stick. In a 1952 finale, divided between the Pirates and White Sox, he hit a solid .292. A lifetime .306 hitter, he led the AL in total hits in 1948, beating out Williams and Boudreau, who both had super seasons. Just one for this forgotten postwar star.

2. The first man to post 20 pinch-hits in a season, he did it in his final bow with the 1936 Browns. Three.

3. The 1945 White Sox had two .300 hitters who did not return in 1946. One we've already encountered elsewhere; the second man was their regular third-sacker—in the AL after a long NL career with the Reds, Braves, Dodgers and Giants. He had better seasons than his .308 in 1945 but none since 1936 when he matched that figure with the Braves. Double.

4. He jumped from the Braves to the Red Sox in 1901 and won 16 games in 316 innings. Born in Wales, this right-hander was an excellent reliever in addition to being a workhorse starter in a career that ended when he was only 29. Yup, a homer.

5. He pitched his first big league game for the 1904 Phils when he was 18 and his last for the 1910 Cards when he was 24. In between he won 66 games, including 14 in his final season when he was the lone bright light on an otherwise humdrum staff. A good hitter, he also played the outfield on occasion, and it remains one of the game's great mysteries why he disappeared so prematurely. This could be your second homer in a row.

6. The 1910 Phils had two 27-year-old right-handers who won 16 and 12 games respectively and who never won another big league game. Although one of them pitched a few games after 1910 and technically doesn't qualify here, they both slipped so unaccountably from the scene that each is included here. In a rare moment of generosity, I'll give you your third homer in a row if you get *either* of these two Phillie enigmas.

7. He led the NL in three-baggers with St. Louis in 1893, then was absent from the big top for four seasons. Surfacing again in 1897 with Louisville, this first-sacker hit .302—his highest average in his final season. Would you believe four homers in a row?

8. Converted to second base in 1925 after a decade as one of the NL's better third-sackers—primarily with the Cards—this 32-year-old Dodger posted 202 hits and a .328 average. Although he played parts of 3 games in 1926, 1925 was for all intents his finale. Back to earth with a double.

9. The NL's outstanding second-sacker from 1908 through the later teens, this Giant topped off a fine career with a .285 season in 1920 and then packed it in while still at his peak as a hitter, though McGraw contended he'd slipped a bit in the field. One.

10. He labored for 13 years in the shadow of Eddie Collins, who was of course indisputably the AL's premier second-sacker. In his final season, with the 1924 Tigers, he hit .303, then left the game only four hits short of the magic 2000 mark. A few years with a contender would have done wonders for his reputation, but even so he had the credentials to earn all-league honors on two occasions. A mere name in the record book to today's fan, he's remembered by those who saw him play as an excellent hit-and-run man and the AL's RBI leader with the Browns in 1916. Double.

11. After a short test with the 1921 Yankees, he returned in 1925 with the Phils and hammered .322 as their regular first-sacker. A good pinch-hitter with fair power, he must have thought he'd found a home at last, but the Phils didn't agree. This one's in the seats with two on.

12. This Cubs' second-sacker capped off the last of three solid seasons with the Bruins in 1922 by hitting .286. A steady fielder, he also played short and broke in at that position with the 1916 White Sox. Homer.

13. After a ten-year absence from the majors, this ex-Brownie won ten games for the 1943 Pirates and posted an excellent 2.98 ERA before dropping once more and finally from view. Grand slam.

8TH INNING
Hose

1. In a 13-year career beginning in 1901, this old southpaw averaged over 20 complete games a season and included 45 shutouts among his 185 wins. Never the strikeout threat Waddell was, he was nonetheless the Rube's chief rival for the title of the AL's king southpaw between 1903 and 1910. In his only Series—against the Cubs—he split two decisions. A single. (Told you it gets harder.)

2. Who was the only pitcher since 1900 to lose 20 games with a pennant winner? It's mean, I know, but this one too is only a single.

3. After nine straight seasons in double figures, he finally broke the 20-game barrier with the 1933 Senators. One of the AL's top lefties for 17 years, his best days were with mediocre Tiger teams. Control was always a problem for this 200-game winner. One.

4. He was the first—and so far only—pitcher to throw a no-hitter in each of his first two full seasons. Still only one.

5. Who was the only hurler since 1900 to twice lead his league in saves and complete games in the same season? Okay, two.

6. Over a two-year period he was 59−9, leading his league both seasons in wins, winning percentage, strikeouts and ERA. In Series action during the same period, however, he was "only" 4−2. One.

7. These two Brownie chuckers fired no-hitters against the White Sox on successive days in 1917. It kills me to have to give you a double, but I'll do it if you get both right.

8. The majors' first outstanding Puerto Rican hurler, he won 18 games for the 1943 Cubs and led the NL in shutouts before going into the service. Returning in 1946, he had little left and was dropped the following season. You deserve two.

9. Who was the last hurler to both win and lose 20 games in the same season? One.

10. One of baseball's true hard-luck guys, he suffered nine consecutive losing seasons between 1926–34 while toiling for four AL teams, none of which managed to break .500. In his finale, with the 1934 White Sox, he dropped 19 games, reminiscent of his 1930 season when he lost a league-leading 20 for the Red Sox and also 1926 when his 18 defeats for the Browns was the AL's worst. I can safely offer a homer, for this hard-luck guy's crowning blow is that today nobody remembers him.

11. A dead arm toppled this Senator hummer in the mid-'60s after he'd become the first modern hurler to strike out 21 batters in a game. Broken-bat single.

12. Between 1906 and 1918 he threw two no-hitters, won 20 for the Braves in 1915, led the NL in winning percentage the following year, and posted a remarkable 20–3 lifetime record in relief. Yet he won a total of only 58 games in a career divided about equally between the Highlanders and Braves. How'd you dig a triple?

13. The first hurler to wear specs on the field in this century, he looked like a cinch for 200 victories when a sick wing stopped him early in the 1928 season after he'd compiled 189 wins. A 20-game winner only once—for the 1926 Pirates—he wasted many of his best years with weak Cardinal and Phillie outfits. Two.

14. He and Young were the one-two punch for the Spiders in the '90s. Four times a 20-game winner, he finished with the 1901 Red Sox. Four.

Potential Hits: 14
Potential Points: 26
Bonus Points: 0

(Answers on Page 139)

9TH INNING
Jack of All Trades

Another new category and one you should knock the top off.

1. This old Cardinal played in fewer than 300 games, but managed to get in at least 15 at every position including pitcher in a four-year career beginning in 1905. Treat yourself to a grandslam.

2. Who are the only two players to play in over 1000 games at each of two different positions (not including two different outfield posts)? You need both for a double.

3. Who came the closest to being a third to play in over 1000 games at each of two different positions? Take two more.

4. Who once won a batting title while playing five different positions and no more than 45 games at any one of them? One.

5. Who was the only pitcher in major league history to win a bat title? Two.

6. After a brief but sensational career as a pitcher with the White Sox in the teens, he developed arm trouble and became a slugging outfielder for the Pirates in the early '20s. In 1922, in only 60 games, he knocked in 75 runs. Three.

7. What Hall of Famer, although regularly a catcher, also frequently played first, third and the outfield, with occasional games at short, second and the mound thrown in? Amazingly, two players exactly fit this description. Equally amazing, you might think, is that you must get both for a double.

8. He led AL batters in triples in 1944. Nine years later he led NL hurlers in walks issued. Single.

9. After winning 138 games, he switched to second base and compiled nearly 2000 hits in a 22-year career ending with the 1906 Phils. Argue if you like, but I'm only giving a single.

10. A Cardinal from 1937 to 1943, he was at various times their regular second-sacker, shortstop and third-baseman— and a solid .280 hitter throughout. Two bases.

11. A pitcher from 1894 through 1902, and twice a 20-game winner, he went to the outfield with the 1903 White Sox and was a regular with them as late as 1912. One of the all-time weird careers. Three.

12. An effective if somewhat wild southpaw, he won ten games for the 1914 A's and as late as 1920 was still almost exclusively a moundsman. In 1921 he entered phase two of his career, hitting .302 as an outfielder/first-baseman for the Reds, a combination he stayed with through 1932. A

This Hall of Famer, although a catcher, also played first, third, outfield, short, second, and pitched, too. (Question 7)

lifetime .301 hitter, his best years were with the Reds and Dodgers. Double.

13. One of the few men in history to perform effectively at both ends of the battery, he broke in with the 1901 Red Sox and finished with the 1913 Braves. Exclusively a pitcher and utility infielder in his early years, he became the Highlanders' backup catcher in 1910. There was nothing else terribly distinguished about his playing stats, but after his active days were over he managed in the 1918 Series. Stretch this into a double.

14. An occasional infielder and a good pinch-hitter, he was through for all intents at 28 after a 22-win season for the St. Louis Feds in 1915. His lifetime winning percentage is a cool .635, mostly with the Giants. A .285 sticker, he played a handful of games with the Braves as late as 1918. The clues are there for an easy two.

Potential Hits: 14
Potential Points: 29
Bonus Points: 3
(Answers on Page 139)

Game

3

You may think you've been all around the league, but there are still a few tricksters you haven't seen. One is coming up in the first inning of your next game.

1ST INNING
Death in the Afternoon

All of the following died while in their prime, some tragically, some ironically, some criminally.

1. After slipping to a career low .264 in 1925, this Giant star was found to have Bright's disease. He put in one more year as a part-time outfielder, then went home to Texas to die at 30. One.

2. Disconsolate over the managerial load he'd been forced to shoulder against his better judgment, this Red Sox gardener swallowed a dose of carbolic acid that had been given him to treat a hand injury and expired during spring training in 1907. Two bases.

3. An unsuccessful emergency appendectomy was performed on this Pirate right-hander in 1949. One base.

4. Found to have cancer in 1963, this Astro righty nevertheless courageously put in a full season of work before succumbing prior to the start of the following season. Two-bagger.

5. One of the NL's finest third-sackers, this Brave was struck down before the 1924 season by an errant automobile. Triple.

6. Another Brave who expired during the off season was this old outfielder who died of typhoid in 1907. Take a homer.

7. The Boston clubs have had more than their share of bad luck. In 1932 the Red Sox lost one of their top moundsmen when he was stabbed to death at a clambake given in his honor only days before he was slated to report for spring training. Two bases.

8. Philadelphia lost its top hurler shortly after his 25th birthday in 1888. In the previous four seasons he'd won over 20 games each time around and in 1886 had led all NL hurlers in ERA. Two-run homer.

9. Despondent over his part in a losing game in Boston,

this Redleg catcher took his own life during the 1940 season. Ironically he'd just gotten his first crack at a starting role a few days earlier when Lombardi was injured. One base.

10. He was slain in the air over Canada after skyjacking a plane late in the 1935 season. One of the Dodgers' top hitters the year before, he'd gone berserk after being farmed out by Stengel. Three.

11. This Indian hurler would unquestionably have made the Hall of Fame had he not contracted tuberculosis in 1910 while still in his prime. He's one of only two pitchers with more than 150 career wins who've posted a lifetime ERA under 2.00. Single.

12. A plane crash killed this ace Cub second-sacker in the winter of 1964. One.

13. After blossoming into one of the NL's standout outfielders in 1921, a year in which he hit .350 and knocked in over 100 runs, this Cardinal star was stricken the following season and died at his Ohio home before the year was out. So unknown is he today that I feel entirely safe in putting up a homer.

14. He might have gone on indefinitely had his health not given out during the 1924 season, his 15th as one of the NL's finest first-sackers. Twice a bat crown winner, he died at 40 in Cincinnati, the town where he labored his last six seasons in the game. One.

15. The Cardinals were grooming this 1956 rookie for a regular outfield job the following season when he was killed over the winter in a Central American plane crash. Two.

Potential Hits: 15
Potential Points: 32
Bonus Points: 1

(*Answers on Page 140*)

2ND INNING
Wine for Water

---

1. After Wagner retired, the Pirates suffered through four dreary years of shortstopping before obtaining this Hall of Famer for the 1921 campaign. For a single, who was he? An extra base for each of the three interim shortstops you can name.

2. Who replaced Cy Perkins? Single.

3. Three members of the $100,000 infield arrived in 1909 and the fourth in 1911. We all know who these four men were, but who were the four men they replaced. One base for each, but no credit for fewer than two.

4. A star in his own right, he replaced Anson as the Cub first-sacker in 1898. In a seven-year career, he averaged .317, including a high of .358 as a rookie in 1895 when he played third. Worth four.

5. He replaced a fading Snider as the Dodgers' center gardener in 1959. One.

6. Whom did Hodges replace as the Dodgers' regular first-sacker? One.

7. In 1913, after some 13 years as the AL's standout defensive catcher, he was replaced by a man who went on to become the AL's finest defensive catcher for the next 13 seasons. A double for the first man, a single for the second, a homer if you know both.

8. Reese and Rizzuto became regulars in 1940 and 1941 respectively. For a single, who'd they replace? You need both men for credit.

9. This longtime Tiger came to the Browns in 1928 as Sisler's replacement. You merit a triple if you remember him.

10. Who did Berra replace as the Yankees' regular backstopper? One.

11. Who made Jim Russell move from left to center field to make room for his rookie bat in 1946? Single.

Potential Hits: 11
Potential Points: 26
Bonus Points: 0

(Answers on Page 140)

You've started to pick up pretty well on my fastballers, but how would you do if I brought in a chucker who dealt from the bottom of the deck, flipping you a spitter or two, maybe even a ... shine ball? Remember who made that one famous?

3RD INNING
The Ignoble
and the Ignominious

1. Well, for a single, who *did* make the shine ball famous?

2. In 1950 his 3.20 ERA was good enough to top his league—the highest ERA ever to top either circuit. Two.

3. What hurler since 1900 suffered the most losses in a season? Three.

4. He led the AL in losses with 21 for the 1906 Red Sox. He dropped seven more in 1907 before being shipped to Providence. His career record was 4−29 despite a respectable 3.35 ERA and a memorable 24-inning clash with Jack Coombs, which he lost, naturally. Two-run homer.

5. In 1953 this Brownie rookie threw a no-hitter. It was his only major league complete game, and midway through the following season he was hurling in Class B. Infield hit.

6. For the wartime A's he was 0−12 in 1945, his first and only season, albeit his ERA was a not-so-bad 3.62. Round-tripper.

7. The all-time worst record for pitchers with over 20 career decisions belongs to this old Athletic righty who in two full seasons and part of a third was 1−24. In 1916 alone his record was 1−19. The true expert would laugh if I gave this more than a double.

8. Who served Maris his 61st homer? This one's so hackneyed by now I offer it only as a change of pace. One.

9. After an erratic but statistically successful career in the early NL, this outfielder was blacklisted for gambling activities. Ironically he was allowed to become an umpire and as such was formally banned from the game when he was caught rendering decisions in favor of the team he had his money on—the only arbiter ever so expelled. Your fly ball down the line drops in for a Chinese homer.

10. In 1930, the year of the bat, only one NL regular (over 400 at-bats) hit under .250. For a three-run homer, who was he?

11. Athletic and Yankee fans of the late '50s and early '60s who got out early enough to watch batting practice will retain vivid mental pictures of this big lean first-baseman

What Cub outfielder in 1969 lost a crucial fly ball in the sun and followed it up by dropping another fly, and was blamed by Durocher for the team's decline? (Question 13)

with the perfect portside swing, but few retain any memory of his name, for once the bell sounded his bat was seldom a factor. Who was this strapping Idahoan whose swing belonged in a picture book and whose average belonged under a microscope? The best clue is he later played with middling success in Japan. Three.

12. This outfielder garnered only 31 big league hits. Yet one of them came on a teeming midsummer night in 1969 when, as a rookie with the Cubs, he hit a last-gasp single to deprive Tom Seaver of a perfect perfomance in a game that many Seaver fans insist is the finest he ever pitched. Four.

13. Another nondescript Cub outfielder in a game against the Mets that same season earned ignominy by losing a crucial fly ball in the sun, then following it up by dropping another fly. Later he was blamed by Durocher not only for blowing that game but for being the catalyst for the Bruins' incredible subsequent slide. Four more.

Potential Hits: 13
Potential Points: 37
Bonus Points: 3

(Answers on Page 140)

You haven't heard from your favorite bench jockey for a while, but don't think I've forgotten you.

This next inning is a real raspberry.

4TH INNING
Who Were They

Not enough to tell me when they played, who they played for, etc. I'm out for blood in this one. You have to name the single most outstanding act or characteristic that distinguished each of the following.

1. Sammy and Solly Drake. One base.
2. Peter Wyshner. Two-bagger.
3. Charlie Faust. Two more.
4. Alabama Pitts. Three-run homer.
5. Bobby Slaybaugh. Triple.
6. Robert Earl Shepard. Tough leg hit.

7. Jackie Price. Take two.

8. Quincy Troupe. Solo homer.

9. Dimitri Ivanovitch Dimitrihoff. You'll earn this grandslam.

10. Larry Le Jeune. Texas-league double.

11. Jim Hughey. Four-bagger.

12. Bob Cain. You might not believe it, but I think this one is worth a four-bagger.

Potential Hits: 12
Potential Points: 33
Bonus Points: 5

(Answers on Page 140)

5TH INNING
Monickers

Breaktime again ... if your mind wasn't permanently destroyed by the last inning, you should be in good shape to score big here.

1. Topsy. Two.

2. Cuckoo. Another deuce.

3. Creepy. Sorry, only one.

4. Blix. Should be a snap, but for some reason it isn't—so I'll give a double.

5. The Apollo of the Box. Take two more.

6. The Antelope. A hard single, I'll concede, but you should nail it.

7. Pud. One.

8. Doctor Strangeglove. The easiest bingle you'll get all season.

9. Poosh 'em Up. Maybe your second easiest single.

10. Mack the Knife. And the knife for you if you don't rap this for a single.

11. Yoyo. Either you remember him or you don't; either way, a double.

12. The Old Woman in the Red Cap. Now you probably think I'm kidding, but if you treat this seriously it's another grandslam in your column.

13. Boze. A triple when your looper gets between two dumdums.

14. Flea. Take another three.

6TH INNING
Ole Man River

1. After years of waiting in the wings, he finally got his chance with the Cards in 1906 at age 34. A year later, toiling in a league-leading 352 innings, he started 39 games and lost 25. The year after that he was gone. Take a homer if you remember this old Redbird they called "Stoney."

2. A one-game trial with the 1922 Browns was his only taste of big-time competition before the Pirates acquired him in 1929 at 33. He won a league-leading 19 games in 1931 and was still effective as late as 1934, his final season. Two-bagger.

3. A longtime star in the Negro leagues, he got his chance in the majors at 31 with the 1953 Pale Hose and had enough stuff left to produce several good seasons, including 1957 when he won 14 for the Orioles and was third in the AL in strikeouts, only seven behind the leader. Hard enough for another deuce.

4. The Red Sox gave him a brief look in 1941 when he was 33, then threw him into their starting rotation a year later. As late as 1946 he won 11 games for the Phils, proving he wasn't strictly a wartime fill-in. This Canadian lefty finished in 1948 and had his top stats with the 1943 Red Sox when he was 11−6. Triple.

5. After several so-so seasons in the early '30s, this smooth-swinging fly chaser was cast adrift, only to bob up once more at age 38 with the 1941 Cards, for whom he hit .341 while appearing in exactly half their games. A deadly pinch-hitter, he played three more years after that and had the unusual distinction of having the same last name as the town in which he was born. A double, if you hustle.

6. The Reds had their share of bombers in the '50s. Among them were these two elder statesmen from the

Negro leagues, one of whom was 34 before he arrived in the majors in 1955 and the other of whom was a 29-year-old rook with the 1952 Braves. The latter was good enough to play regularly on occasion, but both are remembered chiefly for their pinch-hitting exploits. The ex-Brave is high on the all-time pinch-hit list while his partner slugged 16 homers in only 190 at-bats in 1957. Triple for both. One base if only one.

7. This right-hander, appropriately nicknamed "Old Folks," came up at 34 with the 1943 A's after many good seasons in the minors. He was 4−13 but could legitimately have sued the A's for nonsupport. He returned to the minors for several more seasons after 1943 and was probably happier there than if he'd stayed with the apathetic A's. Stretch this one into a triple.

8. Age 30 as a rookie, he lasted 11 seasons and won over 100 games, including two 20-game campaigns. His last appearance was an inning in relief in the 1947 Series. One of a very few hurlers ever to post a career winning percentage of over .700, he twice led the AL in ERA, the second time coming his final season. Sharp single.

9. The Dodgers in the early years of the century were famous for staffing their mound corps with minor league journeymen. This righty didn't see big league daylight until 1907 when he was 33. Three years later he lost 25 games despite a respectable 2.64 ERA. Discarded in 1911, he posted a 43−78 career record, but numbered a remarkable 17 shutouts among his wins. Take four.

10. Arriving at 30 with the 1946 Dodgers, he posted 14 wins as a rook and was their most solid southpaw for nearly six seasons before going to the Cubs in the Pafko deal. Infield hit.

11. The AL bullpen ace in 1944 as a 40-year-old rookie, he lasted two more seasons with the A's and Indians. A two-inning stint with the Cubs in 1942 as a 38-year-old youngster was his only taste of NL competition. In 1944 and '45 he led AL relievers in both wins and losses and in losses only in '46. Three-bagger.

12. The Senators acquired this 31-year-old portsider in 1943 and were pleased when he won in double figures for them in each of the next five seasons. A knuckleballer with good control, he was 9−11 as late as 1949, which he divided between the Senators and White Sox. My heart says a sin-

gle, but some say this is harder than it looks. Maybe so; take a double.

13. Another Senator retread, he was rescued in 1933 after years in the minors ... just in time to get in two shutout innings of Series work. A year later, then 40, he labored in 42 games, mostly in relief, and then was pink-slipped. A grandslam.

14. As a 30-year-old rook, this Cub had only a so-so year in 1889, but over the next three seasons he won an average of 41 games a year, leading the NL in victories on each occasion. Like so many other early-day aces, his effectiveness fell off drastically when the mound was moved back after 1893. Two bases for baseball's last flinger to win 40 games more than once.

15. He shocked the baseball world by narrowly missing 20 wins as a 32-year-old yearling for the 1941 Red Sox. Two years later, after his second successive eight-win season, he was cast adrift. Three.

Potential Hits: 15
Potential Points: 39
Bonus Points: 3

(Answers on Page 141)

(Answers on Page 141)

7TH INNING
One-Year Wonder

The rules are very strict here. All of the following perform-ers played only one season in the majors despite impressive debuts; with one notable exception, none played so much as a single inning before or after their rookie seasons.

1. The Dodgers desperately had the pitching shorts in 1903 and gave this 30-year-old Texan a shot. He responded with 21 wins and 5 shutouts, and that, believe it or not, was his alpha and omega in the majors. You'd like a homer and you've got it.

2. Dividing the 1901 seasons between Milwaukee and Washington, this outfielder hit .311 and led the AL in plate appearances. His 598th at-bat was not only his last of that season but his last ever as a major leaguer. How about four more?

3. The White Sox were touting this third-sacker prior to 1952 as their best since Weaver. After a .265 frosh season he was released. Two.

4. A grandslam and then some if you know the name of the Union Association outfielder with Washington who in his only bigtop season finished third in the batting race with a .336 average.

5. After playing regularly at third all season for the Tigers in 1945, he gave way to Outlaw in the Series. Another round-tripper.

6. And now for our one exception who worked a single inning in 1953 after recording 12−1 stats in 1952, including an amazing 11−1 in relief. My idea is that you're so shell-shocked by now that I can offer up a double for this Cardinal rookie star who was done in by arm trouble.

7. This switch-sticker hit .313 and slugged 18 homers as a rookie gardener for the 1931 Phillies. Name this 32-year-old yearling and you've got your fifth homer in this inning.

8. In 1952 the Pirates gave this 20-year-old rookie first-sacker a shot and he eked out a .220 season in 124 games. The Army claimed him for the next two years and he never returned to the bigs as a player. Yet today he's still a vital member of the Buc organization. Double.

9. This former Little League World Series hero hit .280 for the 1966 Dodgers as a part-time outfielder. That fall he fanned in his only big league Series appearance and although he could not have imagined it then, it was his last major league at-bat. More or less ousted from organized baseball after a fight with his manager in the minors, he drifted to Japan, where he played several years. Worth three.

10. The Indians gave this well-traveled minor league vet a look in 1949 and he bounced from them to the Senators and finally to the Cubs, where he found a home at their first-base slot—for the balance of 1949 anyway. In 111 games he swatted a cozy .279. Three more.

11. The Dodgers made this rookie righty their chief fireman in 1945 and he wound up 7−2 with five saves in 42 games. It was his only look at big league sticks and you're looking at a three-run shot if you can name him.

12. The Yankees' regular first-sacker as a rookie in 1941, he went into the service after the Series that autumn and never returned to the big league scene. End on a double for this one-year flash.

Potential Hits: 12
Potential Points: 38
Bonus Points: 5

(Answers on Page 142)

8TH INNING
The Unrewarded

1. He played regularly in the outfield for five different clubs during the '30s, including the pennant-winning 1938 Cubs. For their crosstown rivals he hit .359 in 1930 and rapped 22 homers, figures he never matched again, though he did succeed in posting a lifetime .300 average. The possesser of a good eye and pretty fair speed, this Texan is forgotten today. A very generous triple.

2. He made his 200th hit in his 30th year and his 1963rd and last in his 53rd. In the interim he thrice led the AL in stolen bases and triples. He missed playing in his only Series when he was swapped to his original team prior to 1958, then returned to the club for whom he'd had his finest years after the 1959 season. Single.

3. From 1947 through 1953 he had six .300 seasons, including a high of .336 in 1948. Relegated to a pinch-hitting role—prematurely, in his opinion—in 1954, he was sold to the Dodgers when he protested too vigorously, and in 1956, his final season, was the final batter in perhaps the most historic Series game ever played. One.

4. A member of the Gas House gang and later with the powerful Giant clubs of the '30s, he was a fine receiver and a good sticker. Near the end of his career he lost something off his stroke and finished with three sub-.200 seasons in his last four years. Still, in 1936, he was good enough to slap .301 for the Giants in over 500 at-bats. Your fourth straight single.

5. From 1886 through 1903 this outfielder compiled a .306 lifetime average on over 2500 hits. Except for a year in the Players League, he was with the Cubs till 1902, when he jumped to the Senators. Another of those rare righty stickers and lefty throwers, he was a cool 7−1 as an occasional moundsman. Breaking the string with two.

6. Migraine headaches curtailed this slugger's career. Although he had the misfortune to play in the same era as Foxx, Gehrig and Greenberg, he still saw All-Star action at first and in 1936 led the AL in RBIs. His final season—with the 1946 Pale Hose—he was only a shadow of the player who for six straight seasons in the '30s had knocked in over 100 runs and four times hit over .330. One.

7. From 1934 through 1937 this Phil gardener was a model of consistency, hitting between .319 and .330 each season. He retired after 1937, then returned briefly in 1945 to the Cubs, his original team as a rook in 1928. Take two.

8. Despite losing three years to the service, he still banged nearly 2400 hits and over 1300 RBIs. Never really a slugger, he had a season homer high of 18 and had almost as many lifetime triples as round-trippers. Thought to be through when he came to the AL, he hit .315 at 39 for the 1955 A's and as late as 1958 was still a valuable part-time outfielder with the Yanks. In five Series. One.

9. Perhaps the slickest fielding first-sacker of baseball's early years, he was 37 before he led the NL in a major offensive category—runs scored—while playing with the 1908 Giants. His greatest years were with the club for whom he acted as a player-manager in 1911, his final year. Rapped .295 lifetime with over 2200 hits. Two.

10. In an era when leagues and franchises folded with the regularity of traveling circuses, this taciturn slugger patrolled the outfield for the same team during a career which spanned 13 seasons. On pennant winners in 1888 and '89, he led the NL in homers in 1891, and as late as 1896 rapped .368. Two for this silent star.

11. Maybe Wilhelm didn't ruin this catcher's career, but he certainly shorted it. A dangerous slugger before the Orioles' acquisition of Hoyt in 1958, he dropped off drastically thereafter due to frequent hand and finger injuries. Even so, he lasted till 1965, rapping 167 career homers in some 13 seasons. Single.

12. The DiMaggios were the most publicized brother act; the Waners were statistically the most successful; but these two sibs formed the greatest brother battery of all time. The

Migraine headaches curtailed this slugger's career.
(Question 6)

catching half caught in more games than any receiver except Lopez, and the moundsman had 190 wins at 30 when his arm gave out. Neither made the Hall of Fame, or even came moderately close, but many batterymen who did had far less in the way of credentials. As an added clue, both had lifetime averages in the .280s, for the pitching brother was one of the finest hitting moundsmen of this century and his elder sib was still strong enough at 42 to stroke .303 as a backup to Evans with the 1947 Senators. You need both for a scratch single.

Potential Hits: 12
Potential Points: 18
Bonus Points: 0

(Answers on Page 142)

9TH INNING
Bonus Busts

Everyone remembers Paul Petit, but there were more than a few other bonus babies who failed to deliver. See how many of these ring your chimes.

1. One of the first highly publicized bonus beauts was this Dodger outfielder who was inked just after World War II and subsequently stung the Bums by refusing to report to the minors after spending most of 1946 on the bench. During that season he got into only 15 games, most of them as a pinch-runner. Two-run homer.

2. This country scam artist burned the Indians for over 100 grand in the early fifties and never appeared in a single big league game. Compared to Lemon and Feller when he was first signed, he had trouble winning even in the low minors. Triple.

3. The Indians sprang for another sizable chunk of green a couple of years later when they inked this Louisville shortstop. He at least gave them a couple of years of service, albeit disappointing. In 71 games between 1955–57 he hit only .210 and had only one extra base hit. Homer.

4. To prove the Tribe front office wasn't the only one guilty of faulty judgment the Yankees dug deep to sign this

Notre Dame shortstop in 1955 and saw so little evidence that he had what it took they shipped him on to their K.C. farm team a couple of years later. Between the two clubs he managed to get in only 64 games, the vast majority of them as a pinch-runner. Three.

5. The Red Sox were sure they had another Pesky when they signed this 19-year-old infielder in 1953. A Pesky he wasn't, though he did manage to stick up top for ten years, all of them as a utility man. Lifetime .221 in 603 games, the bulk of them with the Sox and Senators. Deuce.

6. The Tigers, not to be excluded, sprang big for this Italian-born infielder in 1953. With the Bengals he was pretty much of a flop, but after moving on to the Senators in the late '50s he got in a season or so of regular work at third base. Worth one.

7. Along with Paul Giel, the Giants had a second bonus baby of note in the mid-'50s. It took him six years of trying but eventually he clawed his way into a journeyman role for the Giant, Astro, and Cub teams of the early '60s. A .244 hitter lifetime, he was most competent at second. Just one.

8. Another Giant flop was this big hard-throwing righty whom they were billing as another Mathewson when they signed him in the early '60s. After four dismal trials—the last in 1969—in which he failed to win a single game, they would have been happy if he'd been another Hartung. It hasn't been that long ago, but I'm putting up a triple you've forgotten him.

9. An equally big and equally hard-throwing righthander was this handsome Greek who flopped with several AL teams in the early '50s. Labeled "Can't Miss" when the White Sox corralled him for huge bucks in 1950, his tag now is "Can't Be Recalled." I'm wagering a three-run homer you don't.

10. The Phillies too were guilty of popping for a flop. In 1948 they bid high for this stylish righty but gave up on him two years later when after 30 games, most of them of the mop-up variety, he still was looking for his first win and had an ERA of 6.83. Two-run shot.

11. There were murmurings in 1954 that the Yankees had themselves another Gehrig when they nabbed this huge 18-year-old gateway guardian out of the clutches of a half-dozen other teams. He showed so little, however, that a year or so later they couldn't give him away. After nearly a decade in the minors, he resurfaced long enough to go 0 for 16 in a brief trial with the 1962 Angels. Just one.

12. The Tigers paid plenty for this teenage outfielder in the mid-'50s and couldn't have been faulted too much if they thought they had another Kaline. For in his first real test in 1956 he slapped .319 in 58 games. When he followed with a .214 encore, however, the Bengals grew disenchanted and packed him off to the A's, who sent him down soon after to regions from whence he never returned. You can end big with a grandslam for this Tiger dud.

Potential Hits: 12
Potential Points: 32
Bonus Points: 7

(Answers on Page 142)

Game

4

The next inning separates the men from the boys, the wheat from the chaff, the genuine stars from the spring bloomers. No tricks, no shenanigans, you either do or you don't in your next 16 at-bats.

1ST INNING
Hall of Fame Hokum

1. He played only nine seasons as a regular, compiled less than 1500 hits and had only a .292 lifetime average. Yet he's been in the Hall of Fame since 1946, chiefly because he was the lesser of the two "Heavenly Twins." Single.

2. Despite losing two years to the service, he accumulated over 2300 hits, had a lifetime average of over .300, and for mst of his career was considered the NL's counterpart to Gehringer. He waited till 1975 to make the Hall of Fame.

3. He retired only a handful of hits short of 3000 and was the first to win homer crowns in both leagues. Yet this outfielder had to wait 40 years after he left the game before he was elected to the Hall. Single.

4. In 17 seasons he had a lifetime average of only .281 and never led his league—the AL—in a single offensive category. He, like our first man, was considered a fine defensive outfielder, however, and not too long ago was voted into the Hall. Two-bagger.

5. He had a lifetime average of .341, won three batting titles, and was generally acclaimed as one of the top two hitters in the old Association. This old Louisville outfielder still awaits his election to the Hall, and each year his chances grow slimmer as the memory of him grows dimmer. Two.

6. If the above star is at best only a ghostly memory, his rival for Association hitting honors is even less than that despite registering a .342 career average, including a .373 finale in the Players League, after which he retired at only 31. Triple.

7. He had to wait five years after becoming eligible for the Hall before he was selected, although he achieved during his career a milestone that is considered an automatic ticket of entry. Never too popular with the writers, he might still be waiting were it not for a concentrated effort in his behalf in 1971. One.

8. For nearly 20 years he was one of the game's top infielders. He amassed over 2600 hits and was one of the few shortstops ever to lead in RBIs. He finished with the 1909 White Sox, but his best years were with the Giants. He's not in the Hall, but many who are couldn't carry either his glove or bat. Two.

9. Reduced to being a part-time player by illness for nearly half his career, his main distinction was that he once won a batting title. He was elected a few years back to the Hall—only two years after the man who replaced him as the top outfielder on the team he played for in his prime, a man whose credits far surpassed his but who nevertheless had to wait 20 years after his retirement before being selected. What two men are we talking about? A single, but only if you know both.

10. He was 30 when he made his 500th hit and 44 when he made his 2987th and last. He had to wait until he was 73 before he was picked for the Hall. Two. Rightly, it should only be a single but I'm aware the clues are pretty sketchy.

11. His misfortune was that in his prime he pitched for poor teams and three times led the NL in losses. Yet when he moved on to a contender near the end of his career he had four straight 20-game seasons and finished with nearly 250 career wins. In 13 years he never toiled in fewer than 212 innings, and in 1902 with the Braves he finished 27−20 after working in an amazing 410 innings. This old workhorse has never merited serious Hall of Fame consideration. Your guess why. Two.

12. A broken ankle kayoed this old Giant outfielder while he was still at his peak. In 17 years he collected over 2500 hits and posted a .317 average. An outstanding baserunner, he was still swift enough at 34 to lead the NL in steals in 1900. His name mentioned today is guaranteed to earn a blank stare in most company. Three.

13. Only one other shortstop ever posted a higher lifetime average than this man's .318, and no one since in the NL has hit for more than his .385 in 1935. After quitting while still at the top of his game, he returned briefly in the late '40s to play in his only World Series. Simple single for this forgotten Razorback.

14. In his first six seasons he never hit less than .337. Over a 17-year career he knocked in over 1200 runs. He once won the triple crown; four times he led in homers, thrice in runs scored, and once, oddly enough, in stolen bases. He finished as a pinch-hitter for the wartime Phils, the team for which he had most of his finest hours. Unbelievably, he's still being kept waiting in the wings. One.

15. Excluding batterymen, who is the only man in the Hall with a lifetime average under .260?

16. In 16 seasons, most of them for second-division teams, he won 246 games. Though at his peak as a 27-game winner for the 1904 Highlanders, he did most of his chucking for the Browns. He had 47 career shutouts, 424 complete games, and was still going strong—235 innings in 1912—when he called it quits. The Old Timers' Committee has selected many players with a lot less going for them than this neglected right-hander. To show the extent of his neglect, my guess is that even if I ante up a homer you won't get him.

Potential Hits: 16
Potential Points: 29
Bonus Points: 0

(Answers on Page 142)

2ND INNING
It's All Relative

Your one and only look at this category, so dig in.

1. Who are the only two MVP-winning pitchers who have been caught by their brothers in the majors? You need both for one.

2. This old Senator hurler lived to see two of his sons win batting titles and play in the World Series. The sons are an easy single, but an additional deuce if you know the father's full name.

3. Like the DiMaggios, this family produced three sons who made the majors, all in the early '60s. Unlike the DiMaggios, however, their impact was minimal. Two were pitchers, one primarily with the Braves and the other with the Senators; the eldest brother was a backup catcher with the expansion Angels. Bizarrely, in 1963, the eldest's last season with the Angels, they had a utility man with the same name as that of his younger brother. Three for these forgottens.

4. The miracle Braves had a sub outfielder who later fathered two big league brothers. One patroled the outfield during the '40s with the Dodgers, Cubs and Phils; and the other had several trials at first with the Giants, his last in 1953, when he hit only .169 in 70 games. Three if you know the entire trio; zip for less.

5. Two outfield brothers who arrived on the big league scene in the mid-'20s were Cleo and Roy. Cleo in a 1927 trial with the Red Sox proved a flop, but Roy to this day is a genuine puzzle. In two seasons divided between the Red Sox and Yankees, he averaged .318 and rapped an amazing 18 pinch-hits in only 47 tries. A weak glove kept him from ever finding a permanent position, but still it's strange that no one could find room for his potent bat. Two-run homer for the last name of these two brothers.

6. In the early '40s these two brothers caught for rival AL clubs; the elder of the two is in the Hall of Fame. Easy one.

7. The Dodgers signed both of these southpaw brothers in the '40s and gave each a long look. The younger, a 6'6" fastballer, was around as late as 1952, when he won 5 games in just under 100 innings. Three if you name both. Zilch for less.

8. These two brothers have both been all-league selections in their respective sports—baseball and football. Both played for teams in the same city in 1975, and both spent much of the time on the bench despite the fact that they were still young and still seemingly in possession of all their skills. The parallels could go on, but none would adequately explain why neither of these two gifted athletes has ever fully utilized his extraordinary talent. Single.

9. This Redleg hurler in the late '40s and early '50s had an older brother who caught a couple of dozen games for the White Sox in 1950 and '51. So obscure are these two, I'll give a homer.

10. The Erskine brothers didn't want mom back in Georgia to know they were playing baseball, so they both played

The oldest man ever to win a batting title.
(Question 6)

under a pseudonym. The elder of the two was twice a 20-game winner for the Phils in the teens. Two-bagger for the name this devious twosome played under.

11. For a homer, name the Tiger righty who tied Rommel for the AL lead in losses in 1923 and his son who 28 years later tied for the AL loss lead while toiling for the Browns.

Potential Hits: 11
Potential Points: 29
Bonus Points: 1

(*Answers on Page 142*)

3RD INNING
Outstanding Offenders

1. This pint-size outfielder was a consummate leadoff man for the early Athletic pennant winners. Five times he led the AL in walks, once in thefts, and once in runs scored. His top year as a hitter was in 1901, when he stroked a cool .335 for the Cubs before jumping to the Mackmen. Double.

2. A number of performers have rapped 19 or more pinch-hits in a season, but no other NL'er has done it twice in successive years. He divided his days between the Reds and Bucs and was an occasional regular, along with being the top pinch-swatter of his era. Second on the all-time total pinch-hits list. One.

3. The original "Hack," this Cub gardener hit .352 in 1922 and had a lifetime .323 average in a short but sweet career. Take three.

4. Prior to Cobb's record-shattering 96 thefts in 1915, who held the modern (after 1900) stolen base record? Two.

5. The AL's top hitter in 1961 with a .361 average, he never again came even moderately close to a .300 season. One.

6. He was the oldest man ever to win a batting title. I like this one so much I'll give you a double.

7. The only modern-era stickman to win a batting title while stroking from the right side and throwing southpaw is worth a deuce.

8. Rose and Carew were the last switch-hitters to win bat crowns. A double comes your way if you know what modern-era player was the first.

9. Nine men in history have totaled over 1000 career RBIs without having had a 100 RBI season. They range from _____'s 1299 to _____'s 1015. A single for four right in your nine guesses, a double for six, a homer for seven or more. All nine right and you belong in company I'd be afraid to keep.

10. What early NL batting champ was reduced to a mediocre hitter at best by an 1877 rule change that deprived him of employing his favorite technique of getting a hit, namely bouncing sharp chops that rolled foul before a play could be made on him? One.

11. Who had the lowest average ever to win a NL bat crown? Two.

12. A change in the ground rules extant in this bandbox park made it possible for this old Cub infielder to hit a hokey 27 homers in 1884, a record that stood for 35 years. Even casual historians should nail an easy double.

13. Owen Wilson hit 36 triples in 1912, one of the few batting records that looks as if it may stand forever. Since then only two men have come within ten of his mark, smiting 26 trips in 1914 and 1925 respectively. A homer if you nail both these former Tiger and Pirate slammers; a single, though, if you only get one.

Potential Hits: 13
Potential Points: 28
Bonus Points: 0

(Answers on Page 143)

4TH INNING
Unlikely Hero

---

1. This Cardinal righty leaped to the Mexican League in 1946. Reinstated to the Redbirds in 1949, he rattled off six straight end-of-the-season wins and was 4−2 early in 1950 when he was jettisoned, ostensibly because his ERA was 5.12 despite a winning record. Surprise yourself and put this one in the seats for four.

2. To the amazement of all this BoSox flychaser clubbed .331 in 1931 and slapped 67 doubles—nearly half his career total. The clues, if properly understood, make this an easy single.

3. After failing with the Dodgers, he hooked on with the Indians in time for their 1920 stretch drive and was 7−0. In the Series he haunted his former club by shutting them out in his only start. The following year he started off well but soon ground to a halt and was released. For that half-season, though, in 1920, he was as tough as any hurler in the game. Two bases.

4. A liability in the field, this first-sacker seemed to arrive as a hitter for the Indians in 1965, when he tagged 26 homers to go with a .293 average. He slipped to .241 in 1966, however, and four years later wrapped it up as a spot performer for the Expos. Double.

5. In 1936 this Brownie gardener hit .344 and knocked in 132 runs. A year later he rapped .340 and led the AL in hits. The remainder of his career—which ended in 1941—he struggled with the .250 mark. A nonentity overall, but for two years there he was a near superstar. A head-first slide will bring you a triple.

6. After totaling only 35 homers in his first eight seasons, he erupted for 30 circuit swats with the 1964 Red Sox. It was a one-shot effort, however, for after the 1965 season he was dealt to the Astros and faded quickly. Just one for this Latin infielder.

7. At 32 he got his first chance to play regularly—with the 1958 A's—and responded with 38 homers and a .305 average. He had only one more season as a regular in his 12-year career, which saw him play in only 829 games, a bundle of them as a Yankee pinch-hitter. One.

8. He lived down a good-field no-hit label by socking 17 homers and averaging .285 for the 1962 Angels. The AL's standout second-sacker that year, he gave it a good try again in 1963. A year later, however, he was swapped back to the Indians—his original outfit—and reverted to form, hitting only .241 and slowing down considerably in the field, although only 30. Double for this forgotten All-Star.

9. The Dodger hitting star in the 1959 Series, he also put in his first solid season that year and seemed good for a long time to come. 1962 found him with the expansion Mets, however, and after a lackluster season and a half with them he finished with the Reds in 1963 as a utility infielder and not a very good one. Single.

10. This White Sox reliever led a charmed existence from 1950–52. Although plagued by arm trouble and frequent enemy shellings, he somehow survived to post a career 18–3 record and threw a shutout in his only starting effort. He didn't have much stuff, his control was suspect, but somehow he kept getting his name into the win column, and so will you, for a triple, if you know him.

11. An early-season minor leage performance in which he struck out 27 batters in a game caused the Pirates to rush this 20-year-old phenom into a big league uniform prematurely in 1952. Totally out of his element, he was 1–6, lost confidence, and was never heard from again. Homer.

12. Never more than a fair sticker at best, this Card catcher flamed briefly in 1939 when he rapped an unbelievable .399 in 92 games, narrowly missing enough appearances to qualify for the bat crown. Still active as late as 1948 with the Phils, his only truly productive years were with the Redbirds of the late '30s, for whom he also patrolled the outfield on occasion. Double.

13. He labored ten years with the old Louisville Associations, rising above journeyman status only in 1890 when he led a Players League diluted circuit in batting. Your big clue is that in spite of having an essentially mediocre career, he was the only performer to play in the Association every year that it was a major league. For the true Renaissance fan, an easy double.

Potential Hits: 13
Potential Points: 28
Bonus Points: 0

(Answers on Page 143)

If you've lasted this long, I have to assume it's because you're doing well enough to be voted an ...

5TH INNING
All-Star

1. Who was the first to hit two homers in an All-Star game? Double.

2. His circuit clout in the 14th inning of the 1950 All-Star game is in retrospect generally considered to be the blow that ended the AL's dominance and turned the tables around so that for the next generation the NL reigned supreme. Single.

3. Who was the only hurler to register three All-Star wins? One.

4. In the early years of All-Star competition, hurlers were often allowed to go longer than the present limit of three innings. This Tiger, in 1942, was the last chucker to work five or more innings in a game of regulation length. Homer.

5. What is the only All-Star game in which no hurler on either side worked as many as three innings? Two.

6. What AL flinger went five innings in a losing cause in the memorable 15-inning game in 1967? Two.

7. Between 1967 and 1976 the AL won only one All-Star game. Who was the winning pitcher in that game? One.

8. Who is the only performer to homer for each league in All-Star competition? One.

9. 1949 marked the first appearance of black performers in All-Star competition. There were four of them. You need all four for one.

10. Ruth hit the first AL All-Star homer. For a trey, who hit the first NL homer? As a clue, he also hit the second.

Potential Hits: 10
Potential Points: 18
Bonus Points: 0

(Answers on Page 143)

6TH INNING
Walking Wounded

All of these stars had their careers seriously abbreviated or interrupted by accidents, illnesses or misadventures.

1. Despite losing part of his foot in a hunting accident, he nonetheless saw service with the A's and Indians in the '40s. In 1947, his top season, he stroked .293 as the Tribe's right-fielder. A year later he was the AL's top pinch-hitter. Two.

2. A war victim, he pitched for seven seasons in the AL

and in 1949 won 16 games for the A's with a plate in his leg that made him one of the most bunt-prone hurlers the game's ever had. Single.

3. Another war casualty was this Card second-sacker whose career ended when he lost a leg in combat. Two.

4. Beaned in 1967, Tony Conigliaro never recovered his old form. For a deuce, who was the Angel righty who decked him?

5. What Phillie nearly lost his life in 1949 when a clandestine hotel-room assignation resulted in his being shot? One.

6. When only 26 and seemingly with his whole career ahead of him, this slugging Indian first-sacker suffered a breakdown during the 1970 season and was never able to return to the game. One.

7. Another Indian who was struck down early on was this young third-sacker who was felled by meningitis during the 1964 season. He recovered sufficiently to play several more seasons but never really regained his rookie zip. Single.

8. Perhaps baseball's most ill-fated brothers were this Lake Worth, Florida, pair. The younger of the two, a promising Indian shortstop, was nearly killed in a 1966 fly-ball collision with Leon Wagner and was never quite the same player after that. The elder brother, after nine years in the majors, was discovered during the 1965 season to be suffering from a fatal brain tumor and was forced to retire. The Orioles' regular backstopper at the time, he would have played in his first World Series if he could have hung on one more season. Single, but, as usual, only if you know both.

9. Ironically, the older of the two above brothers was the high school battery mate of baseball's most tragic on-the-field casualty, excepting Chapman. With no more clues than that, can you name this luckless moundsman for a single?

10. Another hunting-accident victim was this swift Cardinal shortstop who nearly shot off his leg in the 1932 off season. It took him the better part of two years to recover, and even after he did he'd lost so much of his former speed and range that he could do no more than hang on for a few more years as a utility man. Three.

11. There were few gamer than this Canadian righthander who survived two grueling years in a prisoner-of-war camp and returned to the A's with enough left to win 13 games in 1946 and 19 the following year. Hit the dirt for two.

12. A midseason beaning ended this White Sox infielder's career in 1954. Only 28 at the time, he already had better than ten seasons in the bigs. His best was 1949, when he played in every game at second for the Pale Hose and smacked .308. He moved on to the Nats the next season in the Scarborough deal and spent time with the A's and Brownies before returning to the Sox for his last season. Totally forgotten today, he was in his time ranked among the AL's premier infielders and before the beaning seemed to need only the stimulus of playing for a contender to really blossom. With all these clues, how can you miss getting a single?

13. Tuberculosis shortened the career of one of the AL's finest outfielders in the late '30s, felling him after he'd put in successive .341 and .330 campaigns for the Senators. Earlier in the decade he'd been a Tiger standout. End with a line single.

Potential Hits: 13
Potential Points: 19
Bonus Points: 0
(Answers on Page 143)

7TH INNING
Hose

---

1. Which of the following posted the most career strikeouts: Dean, Mungo, or Warnecke? One base only ... anybody can guess lucky.

2. In 1951 this AL righty achieved the rare distinction of winning 20 games with a tail-ender. Single.

3. Excluding the years from 1969 on when the league was divided into two divisions, who was the last NL hurler to win 20 for a cellar dweller? Four-bagger.

4. The NL's top winner in 1913 after a fine rookie season the year before, this Phil fireballer jumped to the Feds in

1914 and racked up 40 wins in their two seasons of existence. Returning to the NL in 1916 with the Cubs, he seemed to have lost his touch and disappeared after 1917 at age 28. Three.

5. A second NL lefty who came close to 200 wins without the benefit of a 20-game season, this flinger won his first game in 1947 at 18 but looked to be through at 30. Five years later, however, he won 18 games for the Cards. He lost a season and a half out of his prime, and a chance to play in his first Series, when drafted. One.

6. The record since 1900 for the most consecutive innings by a starter without requiring relief help was set by _____ of the Cubs and Cardinals who started 139 games between 1902 and '05 and finished every one. Two.

7. The Braves in the early '50s had two hard-throwing bonus babies who never did much with them but both went on to post 20-game seasons for other NL teams. Both faded fast, however, and were washed up at 31, returning ironically to the Braves for their final bows. A single, but once more, only if you get both.

8. The most wins by a lefty since Grove's 31 in 1931 was _____ by _____ in _____. One base for each correct answer.

9. This Red Sox righthander threw a no-hitter in 1923 that was tainted when his mound rival doubled but was called out for missing first base. In his next outing he lost his chance at double no-hit fame when his third-sacker fumbled a bounder that everyone except the scorekeeper averred was an error. Two-run homer.

10. One of the few hurlers to successfully make the transition after the mound was moved back to its present distance in 1894, this righthander was around as late as 1901. He won 264 games overall, most of them with second-rate outfits, and six times was a 20-game winner. His best years were with the Phils and with the old Philadelphia Associations. A rather difficult three-bagger.

11. Another chucker who seemed actually to benefit when the mound was moved back, he won 33 games for the Giants in 1894 after a previous career high of ten. Twice more a 20-game winner—in 1896 and '97—he finished with the turn-of-the-century Pirates. Homer.

12. For years this team had the most solid pitching staff in the game, including as it did three Hall of Fame starters. Yet curiously two of those three arms rank one and two in career bases on balls issued. The team's not worth anything, but if you know it you should have little trouble nailing both walk leaders for a single.

13. Orville Overall chalked up 23 wins and a 1.70 ERA for the 1907 Cubs. His victory total was the Bruins' best, but his ERA incredibly was surpassed by four other Cub starters, all of whom worked more than 190 innings. Name that quartet and you have a richly deserved two-run homer. Just a single, though, for three, and zippo for less.

14. By age 28 this righty had posted 131 wins, all of them for mediocre teams. He died prior to the 1903 season, just when his final club—the Tigers—was about to make an upward move. The Bengals' ace in 1902, he scored with two 20-game seasons in the late '90s for a weak Washington franchise. How about a three-run homer to end on?

Potential Hits: 14
Potential Points: 36
Bonus Points: 3

(*Answers on Page 144*)

The season's about half over, so let's take another inventory. If you're over .280 at this point, I'd say you had an excellent shot at finishing somewhere around .300. And by now I think you'll have to agree, .300 is expert's territory.

In any event, now that you're a grizzled vet you should sizzle on your second trip through ...

8TH INNING
The Ignoble and the Ignominious

1. In his last major league start he was knocked out of the box by the underdog Indians in the 1948 pennant-playoff game and was ultimately the losing pitcher. Should be a cinch triple.

2. For a deuce, name the naive young Giant outfielder

Although never formally expelled, this old first-sacker epitomized the corruption that was rife in the World War I era. (Question 3)

who was expelled by Landis after acting as an intermediary in an incredibly clumsy bribe offer made to Phil infielder Heinie Sand.

3. Although never formally expelled from the game, this old first-sacker epitomized the corruption that was rife in the World War I era. Without the stigma still attached to his name, he'd be a shoe-in Hall of Fame selection. As it was, he died of beriberi in 1947 after a quarter-century of living as an alcoholic desert drifter. One.

4. This hurler blew the whistle on an alleged fix cabal that involved Cobb and Speaker. A chop single.

5. The Yankees brought this West Virginia outfielder up for a look in 1915 and saw enough after he'd hit .025, the lowest average in major league history—excepting of course the one- or two-gamers who hit .000. There's absolutely no reason to remember him outside of that one dubious achievement, and I'm betting a grandslam you don't.

6. One base for each member you can name of the old Louisville foursome who were banned from the game after evidence was uncovered that they'd thrown the 1877 pennant to Boston. No credit for fewer than three.

7. After a so-so debut with the 1948 Browns, this tall moundsman dropped back to the minors and subsequently out of baseball. Nicknamed "Blackie," he proved the aptness of that sobriquet a couple of years later when he was implicated in a violent armed robbery on the Coast. Two-run homer.

8. The Cubs' infield in the early '50s was like the little girl with the curl in the middle of her forehead. On their bad days they were known not so affectionately by Cub fans as "Smalley to Miksis to Addison Street." Assuming Miksis had made a decent throw, who in all probability would have handled it? One base.

9. He led the AL in losses for four consecutive seasons, the last in 1961. Never more than a 14-game winner despite having a world of stuff, he operated mainly as a reliever for the 1964 Yankees, the only pennant winner he ever played on. This conversion came too late, however, to halt a downward slide that had begun a year or two earlier after he'd been dealt by his original club to the Indians. Single.

10. In 1945 this Senator rookie center-fielder forgot his sun glasses when he took the field in the ninth inning of a crucial late-season game and subsequently lost a fly ball in the brightness that cost the Senators their last shot at the pennant. Ironically, his unexpectedly fine performance that season had been as responsible as anyone's for carrying the cinderella Nats down to the wire. Four.

11. His one brush with fame in his eight seasons in the bigs came when he hooked up with Feller in a 1938 duel and emerged quietly as the winning pitcher while Rapid Robert was noisily fanning a then record 18. Two.

12. Merkle was never publicly faulted by McGraw for failing to touch second in the historic 1908 game against the Cubs. But he did come in for a bit of castigation four years later after failing to handle a pop foul in a game in which another Giant emerged—unfairly, McGraw always maintained—as the goat. For two, what was the game and who was the goat?

13. This Giant reliever wrestled with his conscience in the late '50s after learning his club was stealing signs illegally and he decided finally he'd prefer not to pitch any longer for an outfit that cheated. The Giants obligingly released him, but as late as 1968 he was still an effective bullpen ace, leading the AL in saves that season while working for the Twins. Take one.

14. The 1968 Series was pretty much decided in the seventh inning of the seventh game when _____'s drive to deep center was misjudged by _____ and allowed to drop for a two-run triple. A single, but you have to correctly fill in both blanks to get it.

Potential Hits: 14
Potential Points: 31
Bonus Points: 4

(Answers on Page 144)

9TH INNING
Jack of All Trades

1. A 25-game winner with the 1898 Giants, he led the NL in fans. Seven years later, now an outfielder with the Reds, he led the NL in hitting and RBIs after posting his fifth consecutive .300 season. Two.

2. Stationed at third for the Twins on opening day in 1965, he dropped a crucial pop in the ninth inning, then won the game with an overtime bingle. The following year he was a regular at second and has since played every diamond position including pitcher and catcher. He waited until 1976 to play on his first pennant winner, though he was on division titlists in 1969 and again in 1975. As an accolade for his all-around value, he received the lone MVP vote in 1967 that didn't go to Yaz. Take one.

3. A rookie at 17 with the 1945 Phils, he was sidelined by a knee injury at 30 and could no longer cut it as a fielder. Not to be stymied, he went to the minors to learn the mysteries of the knuckler and returned for a mound trial, albeit unsuccessfully, with the A's in 1962. One.

4. In 1953 the Pirates briefly employed perhaps the tallest second-baseman in history, then decided the following spring that the infield wasn't his dish and tried him as a flychaser. It took the Orioles, however, to discover his true mettle when they made him into one of the game's top relievers in the early '60s. Still only one to a customer.

5. After a teenage whirl with the Senators, this Baltimore boy burned up the International League for several years as a combination pitcher-outfielder. The Giants, short of portside help, bought him in 1923 exclusively for mound duty, but when his slants began to lose their mystery, McGraw attempted to install him at first only to discover he'd lost his magic bat too. Still ... in 1923 he won 13 games and pounded .427 in frequent pinch-hitting roles. Two.

6. At what position did Billy Goodman play the most games? What position did he play in his only World Series? You need both for one.

7. Although 28 when he first appeared on the mound with the old Association Browns in 1884, this lanky righthander went on to post the best lifetime winning percentage among pitchers who won over 140 games—a cool .696. Between mound appearances he played first and the outfield, seven times appearing in over 100 games. Finished as a player-manager for Brooklyn in the mid-'90s. Two.

8. He began as an infielder with the 1930 Yankees and finished as a pitcher for the wartime Phils and Dodgers. In the interim he compiled nearly 2000 hits and a lifetime .302 average as an outfielder with five AL teams. A deft baserunner, he could also hit with power when needed. A long single.

9. A regular at various times at short, second and center field, he also played over 100 games at third. In 13 seasons he hit only .241 but rapped 176 homers, including 29 for the 1959 Indians, whom he pleasantly surprised after being a throw-in in the Power deal the year before. One.

10. The perennial heir apparent to the Giant first-base job, he was made into a moundsman in 1952 after it became clear he couldn't quite handle big league pitching. After several fine seasons for the White Sox, he went to the Orioles and subsequently to the Indians, where he finished in 1960. Infield scratch.

11. An outfield regular for the Cards in 1946–47, he began the conversion to the mound in 1948. The Pirates saw enough, however, after he'd taken several poundings in 1951 and sent him back out to the pasture, where he patrolled with indifferent success for parts of the next two seasons. Two.

12. Nicknamed "The Little Globetrotter" and reputedly the possessor of an evil eye, he spent five seasons for as many different clubs between 1889 and 1894, playing every position except pitcher and hitting well wherever he went. His glance may have made teammates uneasy, but his overall play had an even more frightening effect on opponents; and it remains a moot question what kind of a career he might have had if he'd played in a less superstitious era. Homer.

13. Between 1929 and 1932 this Redleg hurler led the NL thrice in complete games and a like number of times in pinch-hits. The winner of over 150 career games, he was also the first ever to post more than 100 pinch-hits—all in the NL and none for a pennant winner. A loud huzzah if you don't get a single on this one.

14. A pitcher with so-so results well into his 30s, he became an outfield regular for the Dodgers in 1936, enjoyed six seasons as a regular despite his belated start, and was still an effective part-timer as late as 1944. His top stats were in 1941, when he stroked .319 for the Braves as a 40-year-old. A single, my man, for this the last of several odd numbers you've been questioned about who batted right and threw left.

Potential Hits: 14
Potential Points: 21
Bonus Points: 0

(Answers on Page 144)

Game

5

Wine for Water

1. Expelled from baseball after the 1919 season, this Giant third-sacker's replacement in 1920 was a future Hall of Famer. Name both men and you have a double. Naught if you know only one.

2. He preceded Banks as the Cubs' shortstop. Single.

3. When Lazzeri started to slip, who did the Yanks bring up in 1938 to replace him? One.

4. The Indians dealt Lajoie to the A's before the 1915 season and brought up this rookie replacement who five years later became, for an instant, a legend in his own right. For two, who was he?

5. When the Reds dropped Blasingame after the 1962 season, who did they bring up from their farms to replace him. One.

6. Who did Eddie Mathews replace as a rookie? One.

7. In 1952 Roy McMillan replaced the NL's top fielding shortstop the previous year. Three for this Red gloveman.

8. The Cards swapped Schoendienst to the Giants in 1956 and brought up this rookie to replace him. One base.

9. Who replaced Marty Marion as the Cards' regular shortstop? Two.

10. What Hall of Famer did Bill Terry replace? One.

11. Mize forced what Gas House Ganger to step aside in 1936? One.

12. Chapman's death forced the Indians to rush this rook into the breach just in time for the 1920 stretch drive. He not only helped them to the pennant but was a star for the next decade. Easy deuce.

Potential Hits: 12
Potential Points: 15
Bonus Points: 0

(*Answers on Page 144*)

2ND INNING
Monickers

A breather. You've been working too hard of late.

1. The Mad Russian. Single.
2. Twitchy. Two.
3. Wildfire. Two.
4. Kip. Homer.
5. White Wings. Three
6. Shotgun. (Credit a single for either of two.)
7. The Gladiator. Three
8. Sudden. One.
9. Braggo. Two.
10. The Dixie Thrush. Homer.
11. Steady Eddie. Single.
12. Ozark Ike. One.
13. Chappie. Three. (Disregard all Chapmans; they ain't what I want.)
14. Cupid. One.

Potential Hits.: 14
Potential Points: 29
Bonus Points: 0

(Answers on Page 145)

3RD INNING
Expansion Esoterica

All the questions below refer only to modern expansion teams, commencing in 1961.

1. The most wins by a pitcher for an expansion team in the first year of its existence was 13. For two, who did it?
2. Everyone knows the first and only expansion team to win a pennant, but for one, what was the first club to break .500 for a season?

3. What expansion hurler won an ERA crown in his team's first year of existence? Try for two.

4. By playing in 110 games for the Senators in 1961 and 81 for the Mets a year later, this outfielder became the only player to perform in over half the games played by expansion teams in both leagues in their first year of existence. Double.

5. When the expansion Astros finished eighth in 1962, it marked their skipper's highest comparative finish in seven seasons of heading big league crews. For two, who was this luckless helmsman?

6. What expansion outfit had the best record in its first year of existence? One.

7. Even for an expansion hurler, this righthander had unbelievably awful stats as he posted a 15−46 record in his club's first two years of existence. Single.

8. The first expansion player to win a bat crown is worth one.

9. One more for the first expansion crewman to win a homer crown.

10. A homer comes your way if you know the first expansion player to lead his league in a major offensive category.

Potential Hits: 10
Potential Points: 17
Bonus Points: 0

(Answers on Page 145)

4TH INNING
A Man for Another Season

---

1. Sometimes called "The Human Fire Plug," he played the outfield for the baseball Giants and the backfield for the football Giants in the mid-'40s. Returning for a brief trial with the 1949 Reds, he hit .346. Two.

2. He coached the team that lost to the Browns in their NFL debut, but some 31 years earlier he'd been on a Series winner and hit a neat .359 in fall competition. Single.

This Big Ten All-American signed a huge bonus contract with the Giants in the mid-'50s but won only 11 games in six seasons. (Question 3)

3. This Big Ten All-American signed a huge bonus contract with the Giants in the mid-'50s, but in six seasons, including his finale in the town where he'd known his greatest moments on the gridiron, he won only 11 games. Single.

4. The Yankees outbid the NFL in 1960 to land this Ole Miss signal-caller, but he was a long time in developing and never really did become more than a journeyman backstopper. Single.

5. After starring the previous winter on the hardcourt for the Cleveland Rebels, he enjoyed a fine rookie season in 1947 with the Reds. Eventually he dropped the hoop sport to devote full attention to baseball. A lifetime .290 hitter, he was giving Musial a hard chase for the 1952 bat crown when he broke his hand. Single.

6. He won 24 games for the 1897 Orioles, then disappeared from the scene till 1904, when he returned with the Cards for a brief finale. His brother, who won world fame in another sport, also was considered a top prospect at one time by the Orioles. For two, who were these brothers.

7. This diminutive drop-kicker from pro football's early days had a short infield trial with the 1917 Cubs and wisely returned to the gridiron after hitting only .107. Two.

8. Captain of the 1959 Michigan team and their finest back, he sat out most of his last collegiate season with injuries, then signed with the Phils, for whom he had several lackluster years as an outfielder/first-baseman. Two.

9. If you listened to him tell it, he was the greatest, not only as a ball player, but also as a boxer and a lover; and indeed for a while he made a convincing case for himself, rapping well over .300, although no manager could tolerate his antics long enough to make him a regular. Dropped by the Senators after a .369 season as their occasional first-sacker in 1930, he bobbed up again with the 1932 Braves; but a .238 performance convinced them and everyone else to allow him to pursue his visions of grandeur in other areas of sport and entertainment. Two.

10. This star Michigan State back in the late '50s took a shot at baseball with devastating results. In his only bigtop whirl he went hitless in six at-bats for the 1961 White Sox. Two.

11. His team lost to CCNY by one point in the opening

round of the 1950 NCAA Basketball Tournament; a few years later he came back to coach his alma mater into the NCAA finals three years in a row. In the interim he'd had a shot at the Senators' first-base job, hitting only .191 in a handful of games and showing little of the power that had made him a Southern Association terror. Two.

12. A star Holy Cross halfback under Frank Kavanaugh in the early 1900s, he was one of the AL's top catchers for nearly a decade and remains the only man in history ever to manage back-to-back Series winners without subsequently being elected to the Hall of Fame. Two.

Potential Hits: 12
Potential Points: 20
Bonus Points: 0

(Answers on Page 145)

5TH INNING
Not with a Whimper but with a Bang

1. Who is the only pitcher since 1900 to win 25 or more games in his final season? Single.

2. This old AL second-sacker had only one truly solid year and that, natch, was his last. For the 1920 Browns he played in 153 games and hit .292. Only 26 at the time, he never again appeared in a major league box score. Before coming to the Browns, he saw service with the Yankees and Senators. Two-run homer.

3. The 1911 Senators didn't have much going for them, but their outfield of Milan, Tillie Walker and this right-fielder was first-rate. Our man hit .282 and swiped 29 bases, his highest total in an eight-year career. With the 1908 Red Sox he hit .308, being picked up by them after the Cubs dropped him two years earlier. He last surfaced in 1914, when he briefly managed the Pittsburg Feds. Three.

4. A top-notch performer throughout his career, he threw in the towel after a .307 season for the 1930 Reds. His finest year was 1922 with the Phils, when he rapped .337 and was the league's premier right-fielder. A lifetime .304 hitter, he could no doubt have gone on for a few more years after 1930. Take two.

5. He was 16–8 with the 1903 Pirates when he suffered a breakdown that necessitated his being institutionalized and prevented him from every playing again. It was his second successive 16-victory season, and the Bucs pointed to his loss as the reason they had to overwork Phillippe in the Series and ultimately lost. Triple.

6. He had the distinction of being a 20-game winner in both leagues and also for setting the post-1893 record for most losses in a season when he dropped 35 for the 1897 Cards. In 1906, his finale, he won 14 for the Tigers, hurling in 250 innings, and appeared to be still going strong at 33. Four-bagger.

7. In 1906 this Indian was one of the AL's top four hitters with a .320 average. Dealt to the Red Sox the following season, he not only became their leading hitter but also led all their outfielders in assists. These were his only two seasons, however, as a regular, and after 1907 he was gone. Three-run homer.

8. Kayoed by a bum arm late in the 1891 campaign after having led the NL in ERA and winning percentage, this Giant ace seemed to be just coming into his own when his wing went dead. In 1890—with the New York Players League entry—he teamed with his older brother to form baseball's first outstanding sibling battery. Two-run shot.

9. What A's outfielder was suspended during the 1927 season and never played in the bigs again? He was flirting with the .300 mark at the time of his suspension and two years earlier had hit .356. Homer.

10. In his final year he hit .333 and rapped 210 hits. The AL's finest hot-corner man since Collins and potentially its best ever, he was through at 30. There were, however, extenuating circumstances. Take one.

11. The 1904 Dodgers didn't have much going for them, but they did have this hard-working Staten Island native who won 12 and lost 23 after coming to them from the Giants in the Dahlen deal. His reward for being the staff workhorse was his pink slip at 30. Top winning season was with the 1901 Tigers. Homer.

12. At 27 this lifetime .310 hitter exited from the scene after a .310 finale with the Newark Feds. Not only was he a victim of discrimination against Fed Jumpers, he'd had trouble finding a home with the Pirates as long ago as 1910 after a fine rookie season and inexplicably wasn't retained by the Braves after a .296 year for them in 1912. Small wonder he jumped to the Feds when the chance came. The real wonder is why no one claimed him after the Feds folded. Three.

13. Another player who fell victim to the bias against Fed ringleaders was the player-manager of the Pittsburg Rebels, who posted two fine seasons with them and narrowly missed taking them to the flag in 1915. He had five solid years with the Cards prior to jumping and could easily have been good for another five after the Feds folded, as he was only 29. A two-bagger for this talented outfielder who had the same nickname as the club he managed.

14. At 39 he clubbed .293 as the regular catcher and manager of the 1902 Orioles. It was one of his better seasons, but he had enough others to make the Hall of Fame with ease. Single.

Potential Hits: 14
Potential Points: 40
Bonus Points: 4

(Answers on Page 145)

6TH INNING
The Ignoble
and the Ignominious

1. Who was the first batter ever to strike out more than 100 times in a season? Homer.

2. This Brownie rookie's penchant for plucking opposing hitters in vital parts resulted in a major rule change in 1882 when hit batsmen in the Association were permitted to take their base to prevent him from intimidating them without penalty. Oddly, once the rule went into effect, he faded quickly from the big league scene. The NL, slow as always when it came to change, waited till 1887 to adopt the hit-batsman rule. Grandslammer.

3. What pennant winner in recent years had a regular shortstop who hit .135 and a backup who hit .203? One base for the team; a homer if you can name the team and both players.

4. This old-time catcher had 2335 at-bats without ever hitting a homer and indeed had only 48 extra-base hits. His prime years were with the Association Mets. A two-run homer if you can name this homerless wonder who holds the record for most at-bats without a circuit clout.

5. In 1075 games over 11 years he rapped 832 hits but never had a 400 at-bat season. He finished in 1966 as the only modern player excluding catchers ever to compile over 800 career hits without putting in a full season as a regular. Three for this burly NL gardener.

6. Considered one of the finest fielding center-fielders of all time, he drew raves with his glove wherever he went, but in 514 games with the Red Sox between 1930–30 he hit nary a homer, the most inept power performance ever by a modern player. Three.

7. Gil Hodges went 0 for 21 in the 1952 Series. However, in overall Series action he hit .267. This infielder in three Series, two with the Reds and one with the Yanks, went 0 for 20 overall, although in his last Series at-bat he did manage to knock in a run. With all those clues you should rap an easy double.

8. The lowest lifetime average by a 20th-century player who performed in over 1500 games is owned by this scrappy old Senator shortstop who finished in 1920 with a .218 batting average and a .264 slugging percentage. His top year was .235 in 1911. Double.

9. What pitcher was Rube Marquard's antithesis? Three.

10. This old NL catcher managed to hang on for 11 seasons, the majority of them as the Dodgers' regular backstopper, despite only once managing to hit above .200. Between 1901 and 1911 he played in some 950 games, compiled a lifetime batting average of .170 and had a slugging percentage of barely .200. An excellent defensive player and a fiery team leader, he'll become your fifth roundtripper thus far in this inning if you get him.

11. The lowest winning percentage among hurlers involved in over 60 career decisions belongs to this tall righty who toiled five seasons with the Phils and a part of a sixth with the White Sox in 1948. Though he had a semi-

From 1960 through '67 his strikeout average was a near incredible .404. (Question 14)

respectable relief record of 6−10, as a starter he was a dismal 7−40. In his last complete game, however, in 1946, he threw a shutout. Three.

12. After leading the NL in winning percentage in 1933, this Brave righty suffered through a 4−25 season two years later—the worst modern performance ever for a hurler involved in over 25 decisions in a season. Two for this Brave turnabout.

13. Bet a homer you can't name the Twin bullpen ace in 1963 who was 6−3 with a 1.99 ERA and 21 saves in 66 games. He won only four more lifetime and had only one other save.

14. Indisputably one of the most exciting hitters ever to play the game, he averaged .356 if you counted only those times at bat when he made contact. Unfortunately, in a seven-year career, spanning from 1960 through 1967, contact came all too seldom, for his strikeout average was even higher—a near incredible .404 and a then season record high of 175 in 1963—and no team could afford to carry him, though four tried. For a single, who is this huge slugger?

Potential Hits: 14
Potential Points: 43
Bonus Points: 4

(*Answers on Page 145*)

7TH INNING
One-Year Wonder

If you thought some of the names you encountered in the last inning were obscure, you'll go straight off the wall when you see these.

1. After hitting .279 for openers with the 1942 A's and drawing some mention for Rookie-of-the-Year honors, this third-sacker didn't return to the game after spending the next three years in the service. Three.

2. With the Cards in 1902 he hit .276 in 110 games, mostly at first. He was dropped the following season in favor of a .228 sticker. Grandslam.

3. The Phils in 1936 got a .287 performance and over 400 at-bats out of this rook outfielder and then let him go. Another grandslam.

4. In 110 games in 1925 this Red Sox gardener stroked a neat .313. Nearly a third of his hits were for extra bases. And a third grandslam in a row if you name him.

5. A sore arm idled this Red rook after a strong beginning that found him in the starting rotation for most of the 1960 season. His last bigtop appearance was a single shutout inning in the Series that autumn. Hard enough for three.

6. He led the NL in winning percentage with the 1886 Cubs as he racked up 24 wins as a 22-year-old rookie. Why he was never seen again in big league garb is a puzzle I leave for you to solve. Your fourth potential grandslam in the last six at-bats ... Wow!

7. Sold by the Dodgers to the Indians in 1959, this 31-year-old rookie infielder hit 17 homers, many of them in the heat of the pennant race, then was bounced over the winter after a salary dispute. Two.

8. The Phils, casting about for a replacement for Dolph Camilli, used this slender Irish rook at first base in 1940. In 144 games he rapped .244 and slipped away then as quietly as he'd come. Four.

9. This fleet Coast League flychaser caught on with the Pirates in 1953 and stole 15 bases in 105 games. Unfortunately he only managed a .213 average to go with his speed and even the lowly Pirates felt they couldn't afford to carry his anemic stick any longer. Two.

10. The A's threw this Oklahoma frosh into their starting rotation in 1956, then told him to take a hike after a 1–13 season and a 6.64 ERA. A rugged grandslam, even for A's fans.

11. What tall hard-throwing Buc rook was 8–4 in 31 games in 1958, dividing his time about equally between the bullpen and starting roles? He looked like a real comer but strangely never pitched another game in the bigs. Pirate fans should get four on this.

12. A grandslam for a man who played as recently as 1963? You've got it, kid, if you know this Astro outfielder who played that season in his only big league game. But, wow, whatta game! He went three for three, walked twice, drove home three runs and scored four, all adding up to a perfect 1.000 lifetime average—the best ever among players who batted more than twice in big time competition. Talk about one-year wonders, you've got here the greatest one-game wonder of all time.

Potential Hits: 12
Potential Points: 42
Bonus Points: 18

(Answers on Page 146)

And so, after too many night games and doubleheaders, even my imagination is beginning to drag, and all I can think to say here is that now is when the going gets tough and the tough get going.

In keeping with my nasty habit of never letting you draw a moment's easy breath, I again bring on my number one ...

8TH INNING
Hose

1. In the 1920 World Series there were many curious occurrences, including the only unassisted triple play in fall competition. Take a double if you recall the Dodger hurler whose liner made Wambsganss immortal. Your clue is that along with 18 seasons of solid mound work he averaged an excellent .252 and was a dangerous pinch-hitter.

2. Although nicknamed the "Giant Killer," this lefty actually did his best twirling in the American League, thrice in succession winning 20 games. Some of his best duels were in the mid-teens against his Hall of Fame brother. Single.

3. It's difficult in retrospect to imagine that any hurler in the '30s would not want to toil for the Yankees, but this Ivy Leaguer got so annoyed with the Bombers in 1937 that he jumped them and stayed out of baseball entirely the next two years. In the three seasons before 1937 he won 39 games as a regular member of the Yankee staff. Two.

4. He never got much chance to prove it, but this Oriole reliever was a pretty fair stickman. As a rook in 1966 he rapped .304 and included two homers in his 46 at-bats. Never again did he bat as often or pitch as regularly as he did that first season. Along with his bat exploits, he was

9−7 on the mound in 43 games. Unsung throughout most of his career, he was actually one of the AL's steadiest bullpen workers as late as 1973. Two.

5. A double if you can name all three of the Pale Hose moundsmen who toiled in 70 or more games in 1968. No credit for less.

6. Another of the many young Oriole pitchers plagued early on by arm trouble, he never lived up to the kudos he attracted after his fine 18−13 soph season in 1968. He finished prematurely in 1972 with a 5−2 season for the Braves. Tough single.

7. This used to be a favorite poser, but it's not heard much any more. Hence it's worth a trey if you name the last hurler to start, complete and win both games of a doubleheader. Extra base for the year.

8. Posting 3−10 as an 18-year-old frosh for the 1944 Dodgers, this big righty bounced around for the next twelve seasons, most of them in the minors, before he finally found a permanent hookup with the Indians. Their ace in 1959, he was dealt the following year to the Reds along with Coleman and Martin for Johnny Temple and finished it off with the 1964 Phils. One.

9. The Yanks' top reliever in 1955, he made one of his rare big league starts against them in a crucial Series' game a few years earlier. Easy bingle.

10. This 19-year-old Red Sox rook had pitched only two innings in a single big league game prior to the 1967 Series. The Cards gave the Sox special permission to make him eligible for fall action and he haunted them by turning in two shutout relief stints, making him at that time the first major league pitcher ever to hurl in more Series than regular-season games. A tough trip, but if I added more clues it'd be worth a lot less.

11. You may find it hard to believe, but the last chucker to win 25 or more games three years in succession is *not* in the Hall of Fame. I'll find it even harder to believe if you don't cream this one for an easy single.

12. On his 30th birthday he had only 83 career wins, yet he was a lifetime 300-game winner. Another easy single.

13. Who was the last hurler to both win and lose 20 games as a rook? Four.

9TH INNING
Team Teasers

I've been saving this one for you. A few minutes with it and I think you'll see why.

1. What team in the '20s failed to win the flag despite having seven Hall of Famers in uniform? The team and year are worth a double, but only if you get both. An additional deuce if you can name all seven of their superstars.

2. The 1894 Phils were the original murderers' row. Their three regular outfielders all hit over .400, but their utility outfielder had the highest average of all—.416, good enough to make him the runner-up to Duffy for the bat crown. For one, who were the three regulars, all in the Hall of Fame? Two more for naming the super sub.

3. Excluding the 1915 Federal League race which saw three clubs finish within a half-game of the top, only one club since 1900 has lost the pennant by a half-game or less. One base for the team and year.

4. The Cards in the late '40s were a strong club with a single outstanding weakness. After Kurowski succumbed to arm trouble, they had a run of four different third-sackers from 1948 through 1951, none of whom could make it back for an encore as a regular, with the Cards or anyone else. A single for three of the four. A triple for all four. A homer if, in addition, you can name the only one of the quartet to be selected to the NL All-Star team.

5. In 1906 when the Cubs won a record 116 games, the fourth-place Phils finished an incredible 45½ games out. However, the second- and third-place clubs both played over .600 ball, even though all that earned them was the dubious honor of finishing 20 and 23½ games back respectively. A double if you know both these clubs, but only if you have them in the correct order.

6. In 1944 the Browns won their only pennant while the franchise was based in St. Louis. At that they won by only a single game and would undoubtedly have been bridesmaids at best had their chief rivals not lost a .355-hitting outfielder at midseason to the draft. Take two if you know both the team and the draftee.

7. Legend would have you believe the 1948 Braves won the flag on a diet of Spahn, Sain and enough rain to call for Noah. In actuality, however, they had two other starters who won in double figures, both of whom went on to make crucial Series starts. A single for one of these two; a triple if you recall both.

8. Has there ever been a team that finished in the cellar one year and won the pennant the next? If so, who? If not, what club came the closest? Just one to a customer.

9. The mound-rich Indians were blessed not only with five starters who won in double figures in 1954 but also with three outstanding relievers. Two of that trio will come to mind in a matter of seconds and will earn you a single. Not so the third, who was 7−1 with seven saves. A homer if you get all three.

10. What team had two outfielders who rapped .386 and .383, a catcher who hit .313, a .327-hitting first-sacker, a third baseman who clubbed .342, and a .341-hitting utility man, yet finished in the cellar? Double for the team and year.

11. The war-diluted 1945 Cubs had three catchers of varying degrees of nondescription who saw action in the Series. One base for each and an additional base if you also know their regular prewar catcher who returned from the Service in time to make a single Series' pinch-hitting appearance. No credit for less than two of the four.

12. After spending the first sixty years of this century as a perennial contender and a rare second-division finisher, this team in the last decade and a half has finished above .500 only three times. Single.

13. In this, the most evenly balanced season of all time, the last place club finished only 21 games out of first and only 14 games below .500; the first-place team—although winning the flag by a comfortable seven-game margin—played only .592 ball; and there were only five .300 hitters, none of whom could post more than 189 hits. For a three-bagger, what year are we talking about and who were both the pennant winner and the tail-ender? Nothing doing unless you get all three.

Potential Hits: 13
Potential Points: 34
Bonus Points: 0

(Answers on Page 146)

Game

6

The Unrewarded

1. From 1936 to 1942 this Sooner was one of the AL's top hitters, five times hitting .325 or better, with a high of .342 for the 1940 Browns. Lifetime .311, he finished with the 1943 Tigers and was for nearly a decade perhaps the AL's finest all-around left-fielder. Single.

2. The first NL'er to rap over 200 career homers, he was a league leader in that department at 40 in 1927 after having led for the first time 11 years earlier. One base for this former Cub and Phil star.

3. Before his 4—7 finale with the 1944 Giants he never had a losing season. As a rookie with the 1932 Yankees he was 17—4; five years later, in Indian garb, he posted a record .938 winning percentage. Solid for over a decade despite frequent arm trouble, this tattered sleever's career stats were 142—75. One.

4. In 1931 he was caught by Ernie Lombardi, then a rookie, and in 1909 Willie Keeler played behind him in his final season as a regular. Over 23 seasons he won 247 games and was only the third pitcher in history to appear in over 750 games. An 18-game winner for the 1928 A's at 44, he matched that figure with the 1920 Yankees and had his best stats with the Baltimore Terrapins in 1914, winning 25. Single.

5. In 20 bigtop seasons he won 191 games and appeared in 640. Still an effective reliever in 1953 at 44, he had the dubious distinction of leading the NL in losses with the 1948 Phils and the AL in the same category with the 1940 Senators. On the other side of the ledger, he led the NL in saves as far back as 1935 while a Dodger. Like it or lump it, this knuckleball artist is only worth a single.

6. Named after a fabled Revolutionary War hero, this outfielder patented a children's baseball game after his retirement. Even without those credits he was worth remembering, averaging .300 on the nose in 13 seasons. Top years were with the Reds and Phils. Infield hit.

7. In a career that lasted 19 seasons this receiver performed in six World Series wearing three different AL uniforms and posted a lifetime .284 mark. At his peak, with the Yankees in the early '20s, he was, along with Schalk, the AL's top catcher of his era. One base.

8. These two forgotten 2000-hit men never opposed each other on the field either in regular season or Series play, though their careers were roughly parallel in time and they both played on more than one pennant winner. The AL'er had his finest years with Cleveland in the '20s while the NL'er played over 11 years with the Giants. Both were right-handed all the way and ... oh yes, they shared one other feature in common: they had the same name. Looping single.

9. One of the few authentic power hitters in the dead-ball era immediately prior to Ruth, this NL first-sacker's name hasn't been uttered aloud in a public place in more than a generation. Yet in a 15-year career—starting with the 1907 Cards and ending with the 1921 Phils—he rapped 2148 hits and four more in the 1920 Series. Go for two.

10. Put in the expansion pool by the Phils after the 1968 season, he retired rather than report to the Expos who'd selected him and thus missed a chance to become a 200-game winner. In 14 seasons he totaled 194 victories for three different clubs, none of which ever made it to a Series while he was with it. Already something of a forgotten figure despite being inactive only eight years. Single.

Potential Hits: 10
Potential Points: 11
Bonus Points: 0

(Answers on Page 147)

2ND INNING
Don't Fence Me In

1. Of the five top AL home run hitters in 1947, one never played another major league game, a second played only 31 more games, and a third never played another game in the AL. One base for each of these three sluggers, all of whom were stars for many years before 1947.

2. Who was the last man to lead his league in homers and stolen bases in the same season? Two.

3. Who were the only two modern home run leaders (since 1900) to divide the season in which they led between two teams? Triple for both; single if you know one.

4. His minor league homer exploits are legendary. Less well known is that he was fifth in the AL in homers in 1923 and Ruth's runner-up the following year. Injuries rather than a failure to hit big league pitching were the true reason he spent most of his career in the minors. Two.

5. The expansion Angels were second in the AL in homers in 1961. Playing in tiny Wrigley Field, five men on their club tagged 20 or more round-trippers. A homer if you name all five; a double for four; a big goose egg for less.

6. When Maris hit his 61 homers, he was pursued for much of the season by Mantle, who finished with 54. Not so well remembered is that four other AL'ers in that pitching-diluted expansion year hit more than 40 homers. A deuce for all four; no credit for less.

7. Seven men, starting with Bobby Lowe, have hit four homers in a game. Only one, however, made all four of his the inside-the-park variety. One.

8. And speaking of Lowe, his 1894 Boston club nearly doubled the homer total of its closest rivals. What made the club's performance so remarkable was that its five leading sluggers, Lowe included, were all midgets even by standards of their day. Who were the four other men on this midget murderers' row, none of whom stood taller than Lowe's 5'10" or weighed more than their leader's 168? One base for each; no credit for less than three right.

9. A single if you know who are the only two sluggers to amass over 400 career homers without ever winning a league homer crown.

Potential Hits: 9
Potential Points: 22
Bonus Points: 0

(Answers on Page 147)

3RD INNING
Rookie

1. One of a long parade of Pirate first-sackers in the early years of the century, he tied for the NL lead in RBIs as a frosh in 1906. The following year his RBI total plummeted sharply, and so did he—to the minors. Two-run homer.

2. The Reds obtained this outfielder in 1926 and sat back grinning when he rifled NL pitchers for a .350 average, narrowly missing the bat crown. In the same mold as Albie Pearson, but with even less power, he slumped to .254 the next season and was dumped. Three-bagger.

3. This stylish Coast League vet broke into the NL with a big noise when he finished 14−6 for the 1948 Pirates. His soph season, however, saw his stats turn almost completely around (7−13) and after a shaky start in 1950, he was sent packing. Two.

4. After a cup of java the previous year, he arrived like gangbusters for the Cubs in 1912, winning 26 games in over 300 innings. He repeated as a 20-game winner the next two seasons and was in double figures as late as 1918 with the Dodgers, but never quite matched his rookie promise. Take two.

5. Following in the footsteps of his brother, who was one of the game's early stars, he rocked NL pitching for .341 as a yearling center-fielder with Boston in 1879 and led the league in RBIs and slugging percentage. He tailed off to .275 in 1880, was dropped and did not reappear till 1883, when he put in a season with the Association Mets. The brother clue makes this only worth a double.

6. A lame arm decked this Indian fireballer after he'd racked up 20-game seasons in each of his first three years. As a rook in 1911, he won 23 and led the AL in both ERA and winning percentage. A persistent cat in the face of chronic wing trouble, he was still struggling as late as 1925 when he worked in 25 games for the Senators, the third pennant winner he'd been on, though he never had the luck to appear in an actual Series game. Single.

7. Along with the 1937 Braves, the 1903 Dodgers had the rare distinction of having two rookie 20-game winners. One we've already met elsewhere. This second rook, bearing the weird monicker "Flip Flap," worked only three seasons, leading the NL in losses in 1904. Four-bagger for Flip Flap.

8. Nicknamed the "Hummer," he won 15 games for the 1957 Cubs and tied for second in the NL in strike outs.

Arm ailments finished him soon thereafter, though he was still in there flinging as late as 1963 when he was 2—12 with the Astros. One.

9. Traded to the Angels by the Yanks early in 1961, he hit .288 with 24 homers. The following year he dealt a lethal blow to the sophomore jinx by knocking in 104 runs and rapping .290. He tailed off sharply after that, however, and except for a fair season with the 1965 BoSox, this first-baseman-outfielder never again came close to matching his early form. One.

10. The Reds gave him a shot in 1924 after deciding Sammy Bohne wasn't their answer to Hornsby, and he stroked a neat .322. He was a regular over the next 11 seasons, and although he was never again a .300 hitter, he proved a solid fielder and a good lead-off man. His only Series was with the 1933 Giants. Two.

11. In 1908 the Red Sox found little to recommend in this rookie outfielder after he hit .256 with only one homer and allowed him to drift away. Surfacing again in the NL in 1912, he quickly became one of the most feared sluggers in baseball, perhaps the game's greatest before Ruth. Single.

12. An 18-game winner as a frosh in 1960, he was idled by arm trouble in 1963. In three brief years as a regular starter, this Baby Bird had the distinction of tieing for the most AL wins as a rookie and two seasons later tieing for the most losses. One.

13. In 1952 this rookie Cub receiver spent most of the season among the batting leaders and finished at .290 after a late-season slump. The slump continued unfortunately for the balance of an otherwise unremarkable five-year career, although he showed occasional flashes of his rookie self with the 1954 Pirates. Acquired by the Cubs from the Dodger chain, he was a lefty swinger and had many fine years in the minors before getting his chance. Two.

14. This Red Sox rook gave promise of being their short-stop for many years to come when he hit .283 in 1955. In 1956, however, he was moved to third to make room for Buddin, then restored to short the following year when Buddin proved not to be ready. This shifting around did him little good, and after 1958 he was at best only a mediocre utility man. His lifetime average, despite the cushion provided by his rookie year, was only .249. Two.

15. A really fine rookie season at second for the 1943 Cards was followed by two years in the service. Returning in 1946, he was installed at second ahead of Schoendienst, only to jump to the Mexican League. Past his prime after being reinstated in 1949, he ended as a utility man for the 1951 A's. One can only wonder if that rookie year was for real, for he never had the opportunity to play regularly again. Three.

Potential Hits: 15
Potential Points: 31
Bonus Points: 1

(Answers on Page 147)

The Yankee dynasty lasted for over forty years. During that time the Bombers spawned a seemingly unending stream of All-Stars and near All-Stars. Behind these greats, however, buried away on the bench or in the bullpen, often for years on end, were dozens of performers who saw their whole careers go by while waiting for the Gehrigs, the Ruths, the Dickeys and the Mantles to retire. Let's just test how many of the following you remember.

4TH INNING
Yankee Caddies

1. Perhaps the most renowned victim of the caddy syndrome, he labored six seasons as a late-inning fill-in for the Babe. Nicknamed "Babe Ruth's Legs," he finally got his chance as a regular when dealt to the Reds in 1935, but by then his own legs had eroded from disuse and he was released a year later. Telling you he later became a crack pro golfer makes this worth only a single.

2. He could have been called "Mickey Mantle's Legs" in the early sixties. In three seasons of work he appeared in nearly 200 games as a late-inning replacement for the Mick but got in barely over 100 lifetime at-bats. Two.

3. Catching behind Dickey was a little like being second in command in a one-man army. This Scandinavian back-stopper was with the Bombers for 11 seasons and played on six pennant winners, yet never once managed to appear in a single inning of World Series competition. He's in all the team pictures in the '30s, but you're liable to go through a lot of papers before you find his name in a boxscore. Three.

4. He wasn't really a caddy because for three seasons he was a part of the regular starting rotation, but he holds a distinction that is too unique to ignore. He's the only man ever to play three or more seasons with the Yanks between 1921 and 1964 and not be on a pennant winner. His years of activity were of course 1929 through 1931, and he divided his time about equally between starting roles and the bull-pen. I'll put up four to anyone who can name this lean righty who was 23–24 lifetime, all in pinstripes.

5. Berra was nearly as much of a one-man show as Dickey. For some nine seasons he kept this lefty-swinging Califor-nian on the bench. Nicknamed "Swede," he retired after the 1957 season with the kind of lifetime stats for ten sea-sons that most catchers acquire in one—482 at-bats, a .282 average, and only 209 games behind the plate. Single.

6. The greatest dead-end in all of baseball history was to be a Yankee first-base aspirant in the '30s, but this utility man actually managed to get into 18 games at the initial sack between 1934–37. During the era of the Iron Horse no one else in pinstripes appeared in more. A homer if you recall this Iowa journeyman and an added clue that for most of the 1934 season he was the Yanks' regular third-sacker.

7. Another Bomber utility infielder in the '30s who found little future in playing behind Lazzeri and Crosetti moved on to the Browns in 1938, where he got in four years of regular service at second. Later a National League man-ager for a very brief and very controversial half-season. Two.

8. Rizzuto's understudy in the early '50s and the heir ap-parent to the shortstop job, he hit .327 while in Yankee garb. Dealt to the Orioles in 1954, when it began to seem the Scooter would go on forever, he went subsequently to the White Sox and then the Tigers but never really found a home or matched his early promise. After 1957 he disap-peared, leaving behind a lifetime average some 75 points below his Yankee marks. Homer.

9. In 1965 this fuzzy-cheeked 20-year-old got in 96 games,

This Yankee backstopper, the "Gabber," idled away his best years in the bullpen waiting for Dickey to wear down. (Question 10)

89 of them as a late-inning stand-in for Mantle. During those 96 games he accumulated the incredibly low total of only 27 at-bats. He returned for a time in 1967 as Mantle's second, then disappeared forever. It's been less than a decade ago, but so confident am I that you've forgotten him I'll ante up a homer.

10. Yet another backstopper who idled away his best years in the bullpen waiting for Dickey to wear down was this rugged Pole who was nicknamed the "Gabber." In six seasons with the Bombers during the '30s he averaged only 23 appearances a year. Moving on to the Browns in 1939, he became their regular but was past 30 by then and had little left. A handful of games with the Red Sox in 1940 proved his omega. Three more.

Potential Hits: 10
Potential Points: 17
Bonus Points: 0

(Answers on Page 147)

(Answers on Page 147)

5TH INNING
What Was His Real First Name?

If you got off on "Monickers," you should really fly through this next gem.

1. Bama Rowell. Two.
2. Preacher Roe. One.
3. Schoolboy Rowe. One.
4. BoBo Newsom. One.
5. Minnie Minoso. Three
6. Rip Sewell. Two.
7. Blix Donnelly. Three.
8. Skeeter Webb. Homer.
9. Chico Carrasquel. One.
10. Rusty Staub. Easy, you say? A double says it ain't.
11. Sandy Amoros. Two-run homer.
12. Buddy Myer. Double.

13. KiKi Cuyler. One.
14. Hack Wilson. One.
15. Dooley Womack. Three-run homer.
16. Dode Paskert. Solo shot.
17. Mickey McDermott. Two.
18. Tex Hughson. One.
19. Pinky Higgins. One.
20. Happy Felsch. Three.
21. Turk Lown. Hard single.
22. Baby Doll Jacobson. Homer.
23. Bevo LeBourveau. Grandslam.
24. Dal Maxvill. Homer.
25. Coaker Triplett. Three

Potential Hits: 25
Potential Points: 58
Bonus Points: 6

(Answers on Page 147)

6TH INNING
Ole Man River

1. No one in his right mind would expect you to recall this 36-year-old second-sacker who got a big league reprieve with the 1944 White Sox after a three-game whirl with the Yankees 12 years earlier. But would it jog you a bit if I offered a three-run homer and added that he gave the Wan Hose two pretty fair seasons of work and was a rather dangerous stick in the clutch?

2. How about a two-run job if you can also name this 31-year-old Pale Hose flychaser who had a surprisingly strong .291 inaugural in 1943? Unlike most wartime fill-ins, he survived long enough on the big league scene to finish out the 1946 campaign.

3. This 30-year-old rookie Phil gardener hit .309 in 1932 and went on to play several more solid seasons, including two with Giant pennant winners and part of one with the Gas House Gang. Double.

4. Though he didn't appear in a bigtop boxscore till his

30th year, this old Welsh-born third-sacker managed to get in nearly 1600 games, most of them for the Browns during the century's second decade, and was one of the game's first outstanding switch-hitters. Two.

5. The Indians, topheavy with hill strength, never offered him more than a cursory look at big league bats, but at age 30 he hit it big with the 1954 Tigers and was one of the AL's top relievers for four seasons after that, primarily with the Orioles, twice leading the AL in appearances and once in saves. This tall redhead with the disarming smile was one of baseball's genuine nice guys. Single.

6. Another arm that didn't get to show what it could do until its owner was on the shady side of 30 belonged to this Californian who arrived finally to stay with the 1952 White Sox and proceeded to win 12 games. Two years later he was the bullpen mainstay of the World Champion Giants, and he lasted with them until the late '50s, celebrating his 40th birthday the same year they moved to San Francisco. Single.

7. Age 30 when the Cubs gave him his first real opportunity in 1930, this flychaser went on to register several solid seasons, most of them with the Dodgers, whose small park seemed ideally suited to his line-drive power. In 1932, his top campaign, he hit .319 and clouted 11 homers. And you'll knock a homer too if you know him.

8. He got some long looks from the Giants and Braves in the '30s but never managed to stick. However, the wartime A's gave him a final shot in 1943 when he was in his mid-30s and then sent him on to the Tigers the next year, where he starred for five seasons, giving them their best second-base work since Gehringer. Single.

9. Another '40s star who didn't really become a regular until he was 30 was this old Tiger and Red Sox backstopper who incredibly in 1949, his 40th year, caught 118 games and hit a sturdy .270. One.

10. The 1965 Dodgers, riddled with injuries, handed their left-field post to this 31-year-old minor leaguer who'd been found wanting in three earlier bigtop trials, and he showed his appreciation by rattling off three outstanding seasons for them before being slowed by a broken leg in 1967. Take one.

Despite a belated start, the "Tornado" won 97 games in six seasons. (Question 11)

11. Age 30 in 1903, the year the Cubs gave him the ball and made him their number-one lefty, he knocked off two 20-game seasons in a row, followed by an 18-victory campaign in 1905. Shipped in 1906 to the Reds, he was still good enough to win 19 for them. Despite a belated start, he won 97 games in six seasons and several times was among the NL strikeout leaders. Take three if you remember the slender southy they called "Tornado."

12. After a short Highlander fling in 1909, he came up to stay in 1912 and was 8−12 as a 35-year-old frosh. Three years later, having jumped to the Whales, he won 25 and led the Feds in both victories and winning percentage. He wrapped it up in 1916 after a 4−12 performance for the Cubs. Two-run homer.

13. After a ten-game introduction the previous season, this 33-year-old became the NL's top second-baseman in 1944, a ranking he held till the end of the war. Still around as late as 1948, his top year was 1945, when he hit .302 for the pennant-winning Cubs and formed one of the better keystone combos with Merullo. Two.

14. Appearing in his first big league boxscore at 31, this Athletic shortstop hit .311 as a rookie in 1927 and went on to give the A's four more years of steady service before winding down in the 1932 season, which he divided between the A's and Cleveland. Single.

15. Okay, you saw it coming. Well, here it is: the doozer to end all doozers. The 1931 Red Sox, desperate for infield help, brought up this 32-year-old minor leaguer and installed him for two years at the Fenway hot corner. He never gave them much more than so-so service, but then, considering the quality of his supporting cast, the Sox could hardly have been too disappointed. This lifetime .257 hitter with the "sophisticated" first name will bring you a grandslammer.

Potential Hits: 15
Potential Points: 35
Bonus Points: 8

(Answers on Page 148)

Your next inning is so much harder than it looks that if you can recall all twenty-one of the uniforms these stars were wearing when they first appeared in a big league boxscore, you'll have earned 15 extra base hits.

7TH INNING
Who'd They Come Up With?

1. John Mayberry. Double.
2. Joe Jackson. Single.
3. Lou Piniella. Triple.
4. Charlie Maxwell. Double.
5. Hank Gowdy. Homer.
6. Ryne Duren. Double.
7. Clint Courtney. Single.
8. Hank Thompson. Double.
9. Jim Rivera. Single.
10. Eddie Roush. Homer.
11. Norm Cash. Double.
12. Curt Flood. Single.
13. Eddie Stanky. Double.
14. Gus Triandos. Double.
15. Dixie Walker. Single.
16. Billy Pierce. Triple.
17. Russ Meyer. Double.
18. Claude Osteen. Double.
19. Roger Peckinpaugh. Triple.
20. Mike Marshall. Single.
21. And finally, and of course ... BoBo Newsom. Homer.

Potential Hits: 21
Potential Points: 45
Bonus Points: 0

(Answers on Page 148)

8TH INNING
Jack of All Trades

1. The AL's top pinch-hitter from 1908 through 1911, this Brownie also pitched and played first and the outfield. One

of the tallest players of his era, he showed good power and had a dynamite fastball. In 227 games over four years, he averaged .276, and his failure to last longer or find a regular job is inexplicable. Two-run homer.

2. One of the all-time great journeymen, this Panamanian came up with the Indians in 1964 and after five seasons with them was swapped to the Orioles. In 1966—the only season he ever batted more than 400 times—he stroked .256 while playing all four infield positions and ten games in the outfield. It was in every way a typical year, as his lifetime average was just under .250 and he played over 100 games at four different positions. Even though it's been only four years since his passing from the scene, a double says you don't get him.

3. This AL slugger played regularly at four different positions, including designated hitter, but second base—the position the Nats had slotted for him when they inked him for big bucks in 1954—wasn't one of them. Single.

4. A relief pitcher for most of his ten-year career, split between the Cards and Red Sox, he also got into a number of games behind the bat. At one time his name was the first to come to mind in thinking of men who played both ends of the battery, but it's dimmed a bit over the years. Hence I'm giving two and throwing in the hint that his last big league game was a relief stint in the 1946 Series.

5. The Tigers used this southpaw in the bullpen in 1963. A year later he socked .301 as the Angels' regular right-fielder. A couple of years after that when his bat started to tail off, he was swapped to the Indians, who tried unsuccessfully to move him back to the mound. Not an easy double by any means.

6. He was the Phils regular shortstop in the early '40s, but by 1947 he was operating exclusively behind the bat for the Dodgers. In the Series that year he was a perfect 1.000 hitter, rapping a pinch double. Later a manager with several clubs, he also tried his hand at times at second and third. Only one.

7. From 1916 through 1925 this Dodger was a regular at four different positions—second, short, third and right field. He also got in a few dozen games at first and was a fair pinch-hitter. Third was his best overall position, though he had the arm to do equally well at short or in right. Batting

.294 lifetime in 1377 games, he also played for the Braves, Giants and both Chicago clubs. Two.

8. His first six seasons—1920–25—he always seemed on the verge of claiming the Phils' third-base job as his own, meanwhile playing all the other infield positions and occasional games in the outfield as well. Then in 1926, after Jack Bentley failed in a trial at first, he was given the job and responded with successive .307 and .306 seasons. A year later, after a final fling with the Giants, he was gone. A true jack of all trades, his name appeared on the lineup card at every position except pitcher and catcher. His top year was perhaps 1925, when in only 72 games he rapped .346, added 61 RBIs and was an unreal 6 for 7 as a pinch-hitter. Four.

Potential Hits: 8
Potential Points: 18
Bonus Points: 1

(*Answers on Page 148*)

9TH INNING
The Changing Game

This one looks on the surface to be designed for statisticians, but it's actually a test of your talent for perceiving some of the subtle but significant changes the game has undergone in the last half century.

1. The last year that there were more triples averaged in a game by both teams than homers was _____. Two if you come within one year either way and a homer if you hit it dead center.

2. What was the only year that the combined ERA for both leagues fell under 2.50? This one you must nail exactly for a homer.

3. A single for one year either way and a triple for a bull's-eye if you know the first year that the combined average for home runs in a game by both teams exceeded 1.00.

4. In what season did the average number of stolen bases in a game by both teams fall to an all-time low of 0.53? Triple if right on. Single for one year either way.

5. The last year both teams averaged more than one stolen base a game between them gets you a double if right on and a single if one year either way.

6. The only year that the major league batting average was over .300 is an easy bingle if you give it a little thought.

7. The first season that both teams combined to average less than two errors in a game is worth two. One if within a year either way.

8. In 1930 an obscure Cub righthander named Bob Osborn compiled an ERA of 4.97 in 126.2 innings. What was re-markable about his stats? A triple if you know.

Potential Hits: 8
Potential Points: 21
Bonus Points: 0

(Answers on Page 148)

Game

7

Not with a Whimper but with a Bang

1. A three-run shot for starters if you know the pennant-winning Cubs' regular hot-corner man in 1929. It was his last season and far and away his finest as he rapped .271 in 124 games. Six years earlier, in his only other stint as a regular, he hacked .253 for a draggy Red Sox outfit.

2. The 1947 Pirates may have been the strongest cellar finishers ever assembled. It's hard to believe that a team with Kiner, Greenberg, Cox, Westlake, Roe and Higbe could finish last, but somehow they did. One unremembered clubber who did his best to keep them out of the dungeon was this husky outfielder who pounded out .287 in 109 games before dropping off the big league map. It was his only full season of play. I have a hunch even Buc fans may have trouble netting a homer on this one.

3. An easy single is coming your way if you name this longtime slugger who still had enough left at 39 to sock 18 homers in only 231 at-bats for the 1966 Angels. He failed to show anywhere near that kind of power 16 years earlier as a Red rookie, and the Reds passed him on cheap to another NL club, for which he starred for exactly a decade.

4. The old trickster deals you another one from the bottom of the deck in the form of the Cub outfielder who in 1921, his second and final season of play, rattled off a .377 average in 87 games, including an almost unbelievable 15 for 38 as a pinch-hitter. As a rook he'd hit only .235, but off his soph campaign you might think he would have earned some more playing time somewhere. So it went though for the man they called "Babe.". Four.

5. The Red Sox let this second-sacker get away after he gave them a .312 season in 1933. Only 28 at the time, he'd hit .354 and led the AL in hits while playing for the Indians three years earlier. Deuce.

6. Later a National League umpire and manager, he put together a 22–13 season for the New York Players League entry before bowing out as an active performer. Two years earlier, chucking then for Washington, he led the NL in losses. If I haven't tickled your tubes so far, perhaps telling you he was the ump who rendered the famous Merkle decision will wire you up for a double.

7. The Indians, desperately seeking bullpen help, tried this former Red Sox and Senator righty in the early days of 1959 and then unaccountably dumped him after he'd given them five quick saves and a 1.80 ERA after 18 games of relief work. Never particularly effective before that, he seemed to be coming into his own with the Tribe and was understandably furious when he was let go. Indian fans, who saw their pennant hopes go down the tube because of late-season bullpen failures, were more than a little upset too. Two.

8. It might almost be said this third-sacker got a break when Uncle Sam claimed him from the Phils after the 1943 season while he was still in the pink of form. After five years of plugging away with the hapless Phils, anything must have seemed an improvement. The Phils, needless to say, had to wait for Puddinhead Jones to improve on him. A .282 finale wasn't his best season—that came in 1940 when he stroked .293—but it was well above average, for him and for just about anyone else. A hard deuce.

9. At 40 he was still plenty good enough to hit .279 with the 1899 Reds and lead the NL in pinch-hits. Totally unremembered today, this second-sacker a couple of decades ago was selected to the all-time Reds all-star team, but if a vote were taken now Morgan would probably get the nod, though he hasn't anything close to our man's lifetime stats—2249 hits in 2135 games and a rep for having just about the best glove in the game in his era. Three.

10. After ten campaigns in the NL, he still had enough left to rack up ten wins for the 1945 Bucs. His finest hour came four years earlier when he was 17−12. Broke in with the 1936 Dodgers. Big, with sharp control, the lack of a good fastball kept him from becoming a genuine star. Double.

11. His first chance to play regularly came in the 1913 season, and this 24-year-old Giant third-sacker responded with a .287 average. Oversensitive to gibes about his love life, he quit the game forever after the Series, however, and returned to California. Double.

12. One of the oddest careers in history belonged to this

Oversensitive to gibes about his love life, this Giant third-sacker quit the game forever after the 1913 series. (Question 11)

turn-of-the-century star who in five seasons as a regular was with as many different teams and never played the same position two years in a row. No one will make any claims for him as a fielder—he will undoubtedly forever hold the record for the worst fielding average in a season by a shortstop—but as a hitter his record speaks for itself. In all five of his seasons as a regular he hit .300, including a .320 finale for the 1903 Phils. He played in both leagues, mostly for impoverished teams, and was perhaps the most outstanding of the many gypsy wonders there have been in the majors. Four.

13. The 1945 White Sox have been the outstanding contributors to this category, so what better man to end on than this old wartime outfielder who closed out a four-year chapter as an AL regular with a .293 season—his finest—in 106 games. He was with the Indians for three seasons before joining the Sox. Ride this one for three.

Potential Hits: 13
Potential Points: 34
Bonus Points: 2

(Answers on Page 148)

2ND INNING
Rookie

1. He decked NL pitchers for a cool .339 as a rookie in 1964. Twelve years later he still wields a strong stick and despite bouts with tuberculosis, the police and numerous injuries he's one of a very few active players with a lifetime average over .300. Single.

2. The Indians couldn't be faulted for assuming they'd solved their left-field problem for a few years when this frosh slugger rapped 23 homers in 1970. Both his average and his power production plummeted sharply the following year, however, and when he continued to struggle in the early going in 1972, he was summarily given the heave-ho. I'll gamble three that you've already forgotten him.

3. He treated the Tigers to a .300 season as their yearling shortstop in 1922. The following year he stroked .315, but

fell off quickly after that and finished out a six-year career as a utility man with the 1927 Senators. Homer.

4. When Brohamer injured his hip early in 1975, the Indians inserted this smooth-swinging rook into their second-base slot and he gave them a quiet but neat .292 debut and 19 steals. In return they shipped off Brohamer and gave him the job for 1976. Single.

5. The Red Sox have a long history of rookie wonders who fell apart in their soph seasons. Their second-sacker in 1961 was no exception. A solid .259 opening was followed by a couple of less than so-so seasons and finally oblivion after 1965. Double.

6. Gandil's departure left the ChiSox with a first-base hole that proved quickly filled when this strapping slugger arrived with a big noise in 1921, hitting .304 and clubbing 11 homers. Ten years later he finished out a lifetime .300 career with the Braves. Twenty years after that his son caught briefly for the Pale Hose. Double.

7. The Yankees point to injuries when asked to explain why their rookie shortstop in 1962 never again posted stats even remotely close to his .286, 20 homer, 93 RBI debut. But injuries seemed only part of the story of his slow but steady demise, which culminated in a .195 season in 1968. After a .211 follow-up with the Tigers in 1969 he was gone. Single.

8. Famous for his fielding misadventures, this White Sox flychaser achieved near equal fame for a while with his mace. In a 1930 leadoff, he hit .313 with 16 homers and 114 RBIs. His glove proved too much of a liability, however, and after he slumped to .282 with the 1933 Red Sox he was told to pack his bags. Still, his legend lives on, especially among those in Boston who saw him struggle to play the Fenway wall. Two.

9. Whatever happened to . . . ? is still asked by Kansas City fans whenever this Dominican flychaser's name is mentioned. And no one seems to have the answer why after stoking .301 for the 1962 A's, he fell so quickly and so inexplicably out of favor that he never again played regularly anywhere. Reappeared briefly in the late '60s as a pinch-hitter with the Pirates and Cubs. Just one.

10. A lot of players got their first taste of big league competition when the American League cut the ribbon to open the 1901 season, but few fared better than this White Sox righthander who won 20 games in his inaugural and followed up with 19 in 1902. The first to be called the "Boy Wonder," he'd probably be the last one listed by most White Sox fans in recalling their 20-game winners. So forgotten is he today that I'm completely safe in offering a two-run shot.

11. Take a well-earned three-run homer if you remember the Dodger rookie gardener who hit .329 for openers in 1925, then was dropped after a .296 encore—leaving him with a .314 lifetime average in 246 games! You've got to wonder, given the caliber of those Dodger teams in the '20s, why he wasn't given the chance to do more.

12. In 1963 this White Sox hot-corner man uncorked 22 homers and a .295 in his lid-lifter. His second season was nearly as good, but the dropoff after that borders on the incredible, including as it does several sub-.220 seasons and an ever increasing strikeout total. Finished out the string with the 1970 Yankees. One.

13. Just one year earlier—in 1962—the Twins unveiled an even more impressive frosh third-sacker. A former Kent State star, he rapped .298 as a rook. After a .307 follow-up, however, he went into a slide that brought him four successive sub-.250 seasons between 1965–68. Never much of a long-ball hitter, he wrapped it up with the Indians in 1970. Single.

14. The Astros unveiled a speedy shortstop in 1966 who gave them 49 steals and a .292 average. The following year he sagged to .237, and when a groin injury slowed him in 1968 after he'd been dealt to the Braves he played out the string mostly in utility roles. Like so many who broke in like gangbusters and then quickly faded, he'll be a hard single for you.

15. The 1955 Dodgers came up with two rookie righthanders who were instrumental in getting them into the Series that autumn. One of them was Roger Craig; the other was this Floridian who was nicknamed the "Weasel." In 24 games that season the Weasel was 8–1 overall and 2–0 in his only two starts. He never started another game in the majors, but the following year he entered in relief in the second game of the Series—the longest nine-inning game timewise in Series history—and silenced Yankee bats for seven innings. It was his last brush with fame, for after a couple more very mediocre seasons he was gone. So should you be if you don't knock off a rather easy double.

Potential Hits: 15
Potential Points: 30
Bonus Points: 3

(*Answers on Page 149*)

3RD INNING
Team Teasers

1. When the old American Association folded after the 1891 season, the National League took on its four financially strongest teams and operated as a 12-club circuit in 11 cities for the balance of the 19th century. Only one of those 11 cities has not had a major league franchise since 1900. For a single.

2. Of the remaining ten cities that were a part of the National League structure in 1892, only one other does not currently have a team. Another one.

3. For a two-run homer, name the eight teams that formed the original National League in 1876. Triple for seven. Single for six. No credit for less.

4. What team won a World Championship with an infield that hit for a combined season average of only .210? Two.

5. This team once won a World Championship with only two players who had over 400 at-bats during the regular season. Just one.

6. In 1947 the six top RBI men in the American League were split evenly between the Red Sox and Yankees. Name all six and you have a homer. A mere single, however, for five.

7. The last team that had two pitchers who won 25 or more games apiece incredibly failed to win the pennant. Two for the team. Another deuce for the two hill men.

8. The 1869 Red Stockings were of course the class of all baseball. A single if you remember how the Red Stockings fared in 1876—their first year in the National League.

9. In 1950 this team stole a league low of only 19 bases.

The following season they led the majors in thefts and had the two top base grabbers in their league, each of whom swiped more than the entire 1950 club combined. One for the team. Another deuce for the two speedsters.

10. What two pennant winners tied for stealing the fewest total bases? Each swiped only 26. A deuce if you know either of these two glue-feet nines. A two-run homer for both.

11. What modern club (since 1900) compiled a team slugging average one year of only .261? One for the team. A homer for both the team and year.

12. What team two seasons in a row made fewer than 100 errors? Again, one for the team and a homer if you know both the team and years.

13. In 1967 this team set a modern record when their mound staff fanned an average of 7.24 batters per nine innings. Yet that same staff finished only fifth in team ERA, and the club itself finished eighth! One.

14. Excluding expansion franchises, only one team has never won a league homer crown since 1900. Bingle.

15. First-sacker Phil Todt set an unenviable all-time record for futility when he played regularly six successive seasons for a cellar-dweller. For one, what dismal crew did he play for? For another two, what were the six successive seasons this club finished in the basement? A hint is those six years constituted the sum total of Todt's experience as a big league regular. A second hint is that Judge Landis, doing Todt no favors, made him the property of this team after a monumental dispute.

Potential Hits: 15
Potential Points: 37
Bonus Points: 2
(Answers on Page 149)

4TH INNING
Unlikely Hero

1. For one season—1913—this Pirate was the premier second-sacker in the NL and actually finished third in the batting race with a nifty .317. It was his first year as a

regular, and he had only two others, both totally undistinguished, before the Bucs decided that 1913 performance was a mirage and gave him his walking papers. A two-run homer awaits you.

2. This Oriole mound trio posted only one shutout among them during the 1966 regular season. Yet in the Series they teamed up to blank the Dodgers three games in a row, the first time anything remotely similar had happened in 61 years. Tell me all three and I'lll give you two.

3. A .500 pitcher for most of his 13-year career, he fashioned an unreal 23−5 record in 1963, leading this league in winning percentage. One.

4. This wacky southpaw fashioned a whole career out of a 1962 no-hitter against the Orioles. It came less than a month after his big league inaugural and although he never had another game close to it during the rest of his six-year career, he managed for nearly a decade to convince club owners and Hollywood personalities alike that stardom for him was just around the corner. One.

5. Another who tooted his own horn with good results was this utility infielder, up from the minors for a last shot with the 1954 Indians, who coined the slogan "Win Plenty with ___" in spring training and saw it pay unbelievable dividends when the Tribe not only kept him but proceeded to win an AL record of 111 games. Single.

6. During the 1947 campaign he was one of the NL's most-feared sluggers as he pounded out 36 homers and 107 RBIs with the Giants. Never before or never again did he come close to those figures with the Giants or any of the other clubs he served with. Remembered today on the basis of that one season as a home run hitter, he actually had less than 100 circuit clouts—excluding 1947—in a ten-year career. One.

7. In 1906 and again in 1908 this Dodger first-sacker won the NL home run crown. In the years before, between and after, however, he hit only eight homers, the last his final bigtop hit as a pinch-batter in 1910. Three.

8. In 13 seasons this NL second-sacker compiled a lifetime average of only .257, including a high of .281 in 1967. Yet in Series competition he rapped a mighty .346, appearing in three fall classics. Originally a Pirate chattel, he was dealt before the 1960 season to the club with whom he played the next 12 years. One.

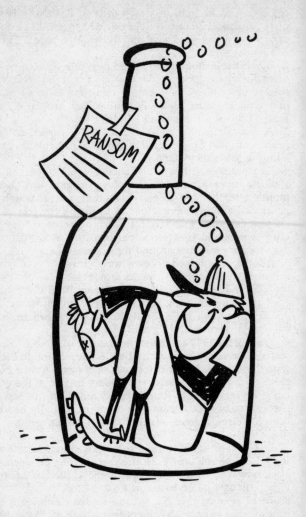

This Card hill ace concocted an apocryphal kidnap tale to account for his absence while on a bender before the 1926 Series. (Question 10)

9. What Red righty led the NL in ERA and winning percentage in 1941 and was the top winner in 1943? As a clue, his only other year of any consequence in a ten-season career was a 12-victory campaign with the 1948 Pirates. Two.

10. The Cards' hill ace in 1926, he concocted an apocryphal kidnap tale to account for his absence while on a bender before the Series that year. He gets an Oscar for imagination but not even an honorable mention on Hall of Fame ballots, for even though he lasted ten more seasons he never again approached his 1926 form. Two.

11. The Tigers thought he was washed up after a 1−5 season in 1965, but he developed a new pitch and came back rejuvenated in 1966 to post a 14−1 record in the NL. Single.

12. Pitching 10−3 in relief for the 1958 Senators, he had 18 saves, a 1.75 ERA and led the AL in games pitched. It was the only season he won more than four games or had an ERA under 4.00. Three.

13. Careful on this one. What outfielder with limited fielding skills was the first man ever to deliver two pinch homers in a World Series? Single.

14. He owns the highest winning percentage among hurlers who had at least ten career decisions, posting an unreal .909 in parts of six seasons in the '50s. After winning five games over the space of a like number of years with the Braves, he moved on to the Cards in 1959, where he was 5−1. In 95 games lifetime, all in relief, he had a good live fastball and always seemed on the verge of really breaking through. Take three.

15. And once again, saving my high hard one for your last at-bat in the inning, I'll ask you what Dodger outfielder hit .319 in 1914 and was third in the NL bat race. In his only other seasons as a regular—1915 with the Buffalo Feds—he hit .293 and then was dumped after showing little for the Tigers the following year. For the 1914 season, though, he was found money for the Dodgers, and you've found a three-run homer if you can name him.

Potential Hits: 15
Potential Points: 30
Bonus Points: 3

(Answers on Page 149)

5TH INNING
Hose

1. A single if you recall the Bruin southpaw who was off to a red-hot 9−0 start in 1967 when the Army ended his season by yanking him out of a big league uniform and throwing him into olive drab.

2. In 1948 his 149 strikeouts were good enough to lead the National League in K's, the last time a whiff king has posted fewer than 150 fans. One.

3. Before McLain, who was the last American League righty to win 30 games? Two.

4. Another single for the name of the last hurler to complete more than 35 games in a season. An extra base if you remember the year.

5. The Red Sox bullpen king in 1967, he won ten games and saved 20 others. He faded badly the following year and was quickly dispatched. Nearly forgotten today, less than a decade later, I'm offering a double if you're one who remembers.

6. He holds the all-time major league record for the fewest hits allowed in a season per nine innings by a chucker in over 200 innings. Two.

7. Name all nine hurlers who've fanned more than 300 men in a season and you'll have yourself another deuce. Single for seven or more.

8. Chalk up a triple by naming the first moundsman who appeared in 80 or more games in a season.

9. Knowing the first reliever to register 20 or more saves in a season is an easy double with a little thought.

10. Probably the worst pitching staff in modern times belonged to the 1956 Senators, who compiled a staff ERA of 5.33 and turned in only one shutout. That shutout and an ERA of 3.60—the only ERA under 5.27 among their starters—belonged to this luckless lefty who made a career of pitching for dreary outfits. Two for him.

11. Hoyt Wilhelm was of course the first chucker to ring up over 100 career relief wins, but for a deuce do you know who the first bullpen ace was to win 50?

12. One final bullpen question before I let you go. Only two men in big league history have toiled in over 600 games without pitching a complete game. One made only two starts in his career, both coming with the Astros in 1963, and the other made only one, a four-inning stint in 1961, his rookie season. With only these sketchy clues see if you can bang a double by naming *either* of these men. I'll ante up a homer if you nail both.

13. Who are the only two lively-ball era (post 1920) hurlers to rack up more than 350 career complete games? Triple for both; single for one.

Potential Hits: 13
Potential Points: 27
Bonus Points: 0

(Answers on Page 150)

Looking for another break about this time? Sorry, this next inning is a real dilly.

6TH INNING
Managerial Meanderings

Some off-speeders here, so rub plenty of pine tar on your hands before you dig in.

1. The only father and son duo to manage for full seasons in the majors is worth one.

2. He managed putrid Phillie clubs in the late '20s and early '30s, then was gone from the catbird's seat for nearly a decade and a half before landing quite unexpectedly in the dugout of an NL pennant winner. One.

3. In his rookie year as a manager he won a pennant, but it happened to be with the Black Sox and he never won another. Still one.

4. Who was the only player-manager in this century to manage back-to-back pennant winners in his first two years at the helm? One.

5. Since 1900 only two managers have won pennants in their first three seasons at the wheel. Oddly, neither of them ever won again. You need both for your fifth successive one-baser.

6. Make it six bingles in a row by naming the only manager to win pennants with three different teams.

7. He holds the all-time record for managerial futility as he sat at the helm of six different clubs for over 20 years and yet not only never won a pennant but never even finished as high as second! All right, all right ... a double.

8. 1950 saw the passing from the managerial scene of Connie Mack and Burt Shotton. With them disappeared probably forever one of the great baseball traditions. A single if you know what it was.

9. Fired after the 1969 season when his team won 88 games, he looked on in what must have been utter amazement as his successor won only 89 games the following year and yet not only was retained but was named manager of the year! Single.

10. We all know that Earl Weaver was the last AL manager to win a pennant without any big league experience as a player. For an infield squibbler, who was the last NL manager?

11. Quick, for a double! Who managed the 1968 World Champs?

12. How about another quick two for the skipper of the 1957 Champs?

13. What was the last year that there were two player-managers in uniform for the full season? A double for the men. Another two for the season.

14. The 1961 Cubs played musical chairs with their manager's seat, shifting four men in and out of the cockpit seemingly on no more than whimsy. A single for three of them. All four will bring you a homer. Less than three gets only a loud huzzah.

Potential Hits: 14
Potential Points: 2
Bonus Points: 0

(Answers on Page 150)

7TH INNING
Outstanding Offenders

1. Since the advent of the lively ball in the early '20s, only one man has ever won a slugging crown with a percentage of under .500. Who for two?

2. Between 1955 and 1963 this Pennsylvania traveler set a modern record for being on a merry-go-round when he saw regular duty at the hot corner for five different NL teams, two of them pennant winners. A bit short on talent, but long on competitive drive. One.

3. The AL steal champ in 1950, he had only 15—the all-time major league record low for a leader. One.

4. In 1948 Keltner had his finest year and made the AL All-Star squad with ease as he rapped out .297 and 119 RBIs for the pennant-winning Indians. Yet an unheralded Athletic third-sacker who got no All-Star attention actually did him better, stroking a neat .310 and bringing home 120 mates. Staten Islanders get an easy bingle.

5. In 1941, amid the likes of Ott, Mize, Nicholson and Camilli, this swinger led the NL in slugging percentage despite registering only 14 homers. Two.

6. He was the last man to garner more than 150 walks in a season. For one, who was he? For another deuce, when did he do it?

7. What clouter once led the AL in slugging percentage on only a .258 batting average? Hard single.

8. Who was the first major league triple crown winner? Four.

9. Who was the AL's first triple crown winner? One.

10. Who was the only triple crown winner also to lead his league in stolen bases? One.

11. Two bases if you can name the last player to score more than 150 runs in a season and another deuce for the year he did it.

12. This Brownie gardener stunned the baseball world when he homered in his first two major league at-bats in 1951. Eleven years later, in his last bigtop at-bat, he walked in his one and only Series appearance. Take. one.

13. The Cardinals owned the best pinch-swingers in baseball in both 1953 and 1954 and were the first team in history that had pinch-stickers who recorded 20 or more pinch bingles in successive years. Their 1953 ace delivered 22 clutch raps, tieing a major league record, then dropped off to only seven the following season. However, the slack was more than taken up by a perennial minor leaguer, nick-

named "Cobra," who was given a final shot at the bigs in 1954 and responded with 20 pinch raps, still a rookie record. Name both and get three. You draw a blank, however, if you know only one.

14. Had either Fred Lynn or Jim Rice driven in 100 or more runs in 1976, it would have been the first time in over 20 years that anyone had racked up 100 ribbies in his first two seasons in the bigs. For a rugged trey, who was the last man to do it?

Potential Hits: 14
Potential Points: 25
Bonus Points: 0

(Answers on Page 150)

With the season ending and fall rapidly approaching, your final two innings should put you in the mood ...

TH INNING
A Man for Another Season

1. Who is the only man ever to pitch in a World Series and play on an NBA Championship team? So easy I'm embarrassed even to give a single.

2. In the late '40s the Cubs took a long look at this husky former Packer fullback. An outfielder, he played parts of three seasons with them and ended with a .251 average in 63 games. Homer.

3. Stanford's finest postwar tailback chose baseball over pro football. Nicknamed "Citation," he proved a good baserunner but his stick left something to be desired. Over a five-year career, beginning in 1949, he hit only .242. The Reds' regular center-fielder for a time. Two.

4. Dayton University's top forward and rebounder in the early '60s was this lanky lefty from Cleveland. Baseball seemed to offer him more than the NBA, and he signed with the Twins. After a promising 1963 debut, arm trouble wrecked what might have been an outstanding mound career, though he was still plugging away with the Red Sox in the late '60s. Three.

5. This Duke backcourt whiz is the only man ever to be a hardwood All-American and a major league MVP. Single.

6. Another court All-American who finished high up several times in MVP balloting was this hulking Ohio Stater who skipped his senior year in 1958 to take a huge slice of big league cash. Single.

7. Indiana's Big Nine championship eleven in 1946 had two bruising ends who went on to great pro careers, one in football and the other in baseball. The footballer was of course Pete Pihos. The baseballer clubbed 279 lifetime homers, the last with the expansion Angels in 1961. One.

8. These twins starred for Seattle University's basketball team in the early '50s and later formed a keystone combo for the 1953 Pirates. Both had strong arms and sure gloves but suffered equally from weak sticks, and curiously each after failing in numerous infield trials took a whirl as a moundsman. One.

9. It's long been maintained that almost the first quality Woodie Hayes looks for in a quarterback is an inability to pass, but this OSU signal-caller had such a fine arm that he was later signed by the Tigers for their mound corps and gave them several solid seasons, including a 16−9 in 1967. Just one.

10. An All-American forward at Duquesne in the '50s, he was given many mound trials by the Cards but never quite connected. Pitching 1−6 lifetime, all his decisions coming in 1959, he had a younger brother who later caught for the Redbirds. Two.

11. Co-captain and fullback on the 1959 Rose Bowl winner, he was 6−19 six years later with the Mets and 25−56 lifetime, ending with the 1969 A's. Double.

12. This smooth-shooting Southeastern Conference All-American in the '60s chose baseball over the NBA with dire consequences. A first-sacker, he managed only three hits in sixteen at-bats in trials with the White Sox and Twins. One.

13. The only man ever to play on an NCAA court champ and pitch in the majors, he accomplished both in 1961. Even with the year as a clue, you'll still have trouble getting three for this former Senator.

14. This should have been a good inning for you, and to top it off for a bunt single all you need do is name the former Indian and Brownie infielder in the '40s with the matinee profile who went on to a long Hollywood career and starred for many years on a popular daytime serial.

9TH INNING
Fall Classic

1. Seven pitchers in Series history have thrown three complete winning games in a single Series. Only one, however, has hurled three shutouts. Single.

2. In the 1947 Series three men who never again performed in a regular season game accomplished historic Series feats. Who were they? What were their feats? Bunt single for all three. A most ignominious strikeout for anything less.

3. In the 1946 Series Pesky was accused of holding the relay too long after _____'s hit, permitting Slaughter to score the winning run in the 7th game. Forgotten is that _____ was the hitting star of the Series. For two bases, who was he?

4. What was the last Series in which no home runs were hit? Three.

5. Who was the last player-manager to appear in a Series? One.

6. What was the last Series between two teams using the same park? One.

7. Who were the first brothers to play against each other in a Series? Homer.

8. Excluding expansion teams, what is the only franchise never to win a World Series? Single.

9. He was the only member of Pro Football's Hall of Fame to play in a Series. Single.

10. What Red Sox hurler won three games in his first Series, then several years later, in his second Series, hit .200 as an outfielder for another AL team? Single.

Game 1

Rookie

1. Jim Finegan. 2. Jim Turner and Lou Fette. 3. Chuck Hostetler. 4. Beauty Beaumont. 5. Noodles Hahn. 6. Dickie Kerr. 7. Sam Mele. 8. Johnny Rizzo. 9. Bob Rodgers. 10. Johnny Beazley. 11. Mattie Kilroy. 12. Johnny Pesky. 13. Lou Skizas. 14. Dick Wakefield. 15. Roscoe Miller.

2ND INNING
Ole Man River

1. Dazzy Vance. 2. Lance Richbourg. 3. Bob Keegan. 4. Bob Wood. 5. Eddie Brown. 6. Earl Brucker. 7. Joe Start. 8. Ellis Kinder. 9. Remy Kremer. 10. Diomedes Olivo. 11. George Harper. 12. Joe Marris. 13. Mike Guerra. 14. Showboat Fisher. 15. Joe Heving.

3RD INNING
Hose

1. 28, Robin Roberts, 1952. 2. Tex Hughson. 3. Jim Hughes. 4. Johhny Klippstein. 5. Jack Kramer. 6. Howie Krist. 7. Wild Bill Donovan. 8. Tacks Neuer. 9. Frank Smith. 10. Ike Delock 11. DiMaggio, Hornsby, Delahanty and Goslin. 12. George Uhle. 13. Sal Maglie. 14. Hank Borowy.

4TH INNING
Not with a Whimper but with a Bang

1. Sam Dungan 2. Eldon Auker. 3. Smokey Joe Wood. 4. Buddy Hassett. 5. Johnny Dickshot. 6. Jack Graham. 7. Pop Foster. 8. Slug Burns. 9. Augie Bergamo. 10. Larry French. 11. Russ Christopher. 12. Cal McVey. 13. Hooks Dauss.

5TH INNING
The Unrewarded

1. Duke Farrell. 2. Steve Evans. 3. Lave Cross. 4. Bob Johnson. 5. Paul Hines. 6. Walker Cooper. 7. Lipman Pike. 8. Sam Jones. 9. Sam Leever. 10. Barney McCosky. 11. Eddie McKean. 12. Ted Easterly.

6TH INNING
Unlikely Hero

1. Pat Seerey. **2.** Al Wingo. **3.** Tito Francona. **4.** Bob Hazle. **5.** Floyd Giebell. **6.** Debs Garms. **7.** Dick Burrus. **8.** Bill Sweeney. **9.** Deron Johnson. **10.** Bill Hinchman. **11.** Dale Alexander. **12.** Jack Knight. **13.** Danny Cater.

7TH INNING
Outstanding Offenders

1. Nellie Fox. **2.** Eddie Yost. **3.** Carl Yastrzemski, Tommy Davis, Pete Runnels, Mickey Vernon and Ferris Fain. **4.** Joe Jackson, .408 in 1911. **5.** Ham Hyatt, the old Pirate outfielder. **6.** Dutch Zwilling (in the two years the Federal League operated he amassed both the most total homers and RBIs.). **7.** Fred Dunlap. **8.** Jake Stenzel. **9.** Woodie Jensen. **10.** Ernie Lombardi. **11.** Jesse Burkett. **12.** Roy Thomas. **13.** Roger Connor. **14.** Smokey Burgess.

8TH INNING
Wine for Water

1. Sammy Vick. **2.** Duff Cooley. **3.** Wallie Pipp. **4.** Babe Dahlgren. **5.** Ben Chapman. **6.** Cass Michaels. **7.** Jake Powell. **8.** Bobbie Thomson. **9.** Willie Mays. **10.** Frank Thomas. **11.** Harry Walker.

9TH INNING
Fall Classic

1. Deacon Phillippe, in 1903. **2.** Jimmy Sebring. **3.** Lefty Williams, in 1919. **4.** The 1960 Pirates. **5.** Larry Sherry. **6.** Patsy Dougherty, 1903. **7.** Jack Sheehan, with the 1920 Dodgers. **8.** The Dodgers hit .142 in 1966. **9.** The 1960 Yankees. **10.** Dal Maxvill, in 1968. **11.** Boss Schmidt, with the 1907 Tigers.

Game 2

1ST INNING
Don't Fence Me In

1. Tommy Holmes, in 1945. **2.** Fred Odwell, truly an oddie. **3.** Dave Brain. **4.** Gavvy Cravath, in 1919. **5.** Rocky Colavito, in 1958. **6.** Home Run Baker. **7.** Nope,

not Cy Williams or Hack Wilson ... 'twas Rogers
Hornsby in 1922. **8.** All seven; you could look it up.
9. Mickey Mantle, in 1960.

2ND INNING
Monickers

1. Charles Baldwin. **2.** Charles Hickman. **3.** Lynn
Nelson. **4.** Hubert Pruett, Ruth's old nemesis. **5.** John
Healy. **6.** Prentice Browne. **7.** Lewis McAllister. **8.** Rudy
Regalado. **9.** Forrest Jacobs. **10.** James Callahan. **11.** Bill
Wolf and Nelson Hawks. **12.** Harold Valentine.
13. Frank Overmire. **14.** Inman Veal.

3RD INNING
Metomania

1. Al Moran. **2.** Craig Anderson. **3.** A little tricky, I'll
agree, as the Metsies have *never* had an offensive leader
in anything. **4.** Jerry Koosman, 19, 1968. **5.** Bob Shaw
and Dennis Ribant. **6.** Charlie Smith, 1964−65; and
Wayne Garrett, 1973−74. Ed Charles, it's true, played
semi-regularly in 1967−68, but in neither season did he
compile 400 at-bats. **7.** Roy Stanton. **8.** Ron Hunt and
Joe Christopher. **9.** Amos Otis. **10.** Rusty Staub had 105
in 1975.

4TH INNING
Rookie

1. George Watkins. **2.** Jimmy Williams. **3.** Taffy Wright.
4. Walt Dropo. **5.** Patsy Dougherty. **6.** Erve Beck. **7.** Jim
Dyck. **8.** Harry Lumley. **9.** Paul Smith. **10.** Ted Wilks.
11. Chet Nichols. **12.** Clint Hartung. **13.** Chief Johnson.
14. Tom Umphlett. **15.** Von McDaniel, and, of course,
Lindy.

5TH INNING
The Unrewarded

1. Deacon and Will White. **2.** Ken Williams. **3.** Patsy and
Wild Bill Donovan. **4.** Mike Donlin. **5.** Bobbie Doerr.
6. Bubbles Hargrave. **7.** Jeff Heath. **8.** Harvey Hendrick.
9. Sam Leslie. **10.** Sherry Magee. **11.** George Blaeholder.
12. Cecil Travis.

6TH INNING
A Man for Another Season

1. Vic Janowicz. 2. Thorpe, Nevers, Halas, Driscoll and Ace Parker; two-run homer for all five. 3. Pete Layden. 4. Eric Tipton. 5. Carroll Hardy. 6. Ken Harrelson. 7. Doc Prothro. 8. Harry Agganis and Jim Gastall. 9. Ron Reed and Dave DeBusschere. 10. Wynn Hawkins. 11. Haywood Sullivan. 12. Jim Castiglia. 13. Larry Isbell.

7TH INNING
Not with a Whimper but with a Bang

1. Bob Dillinger. 2. Ed Coleman. 3. Tony Cuccinello. 4. Ted Lewis. 5. Johnny Lush. 6. Lew Moren and Bob Ewing. 7. Percy Werden. 8. Milt Stock. 9. Larry Doyle. 10. Del Pratt. 11. Chicken Hawks. 12. Zeb Terry. 13. Wallie Hebert.

8TH INNING
Hose

1. Doc White. 2. George Mullin, with the 1907 Tigers. 3. Earl Whitehill. 4. Steve Busby. 5. Three Finger Brown, 1909–10. 6. Lefty Grove, 1930–31. 7. Bob Groom and Ernie Koob. 8. Hi Bithorn. 9. Wilbur Wood, 1973. 10. Milt Gaston. 11. Tom Cheney. 12. Tom Hughes. 13. Lee Meadows. 14. Nig Cuppy.

9TH INNING
Jack of All Trades

1. Art Hoelskoetter. 2. Stan Musial and Ernie Banks; Musial first and the outfield, Banks first and short. 3. Tommy Leach, 1078 games in the outfield and 955 at third. 4. Billy Goodman, 45 games in the outfield and a scattering of games at all four infield positions. 5. Guy Hecker, 1886 American Association. 6. Reb Russell. 7. Buck Ewing and Roger Bresnahan. 8. Johnny Lindell. 9. Kid Gleason. 10. Jimmy Brown. 11. Nixey Callahan. 12. Rube Bressler. 13. Fred Mitchell. 14. Doc Crandall.

Game 3

1ST INNING
Death in the Afternoon

1. Ross Youngs. **2.** Chick Stahl. **3.** Tiny Bonham. **4.** Jim Umbricht. **5.** Tony Boeckel. **6.** Cozy Dolan. **7.** Ed Morris. **8.** Charlie Ferguson. **9.** Willard Hershberger. **10.** Len Koenecke. **11.** Addie Joss. **12.** Ken Hubbs. **13.** Austin McHenry. **14.** Jake Daubert. **15.** Charlie Peete.

2ND INNING
Wine for Water

1. Rabbit Maranville—the interims were the unforgettables Chuck Ward, Buster Caton and Zeb Terry. **2.** Mickey Cochrane. **3.** Harry Davis at first, Danny Murphy at second, Simon Nicholls at short and Jimmy Collins at third. **4.** Bill Everett. **5.** Don Demeter. **6.** Jackie Robinson; Robbie, you'll recall, played first as a rook. **7.** Billy Sullivan and Ray Schalk. **8.** Durocher and Crosetti. **9.** Lu Blue. **10.** Aaron Robinson. **11.** Ralph Kiner.

3RD INNING
The Ignoble and the Ignominious

1. Eddie Cicotte. **2.** Early Wynn. **3.** Vic Willis, 29 with the 1905 Braves. **4.** Joe Harris. **5.** BoBo Holloman. **6.** Steve Gerkin. **7.** Jack Nabors. **8.** Tracy Stallard. **9.** Dick Higham. **10.** Hod Ford of the Reds hit .231. **11.** Kent Hadley. **12.** Jim Qualls. **13.** Don Young.

4TH INNING
Who Were They

1. The first black siblings to play in the majors since the fabled Walkers with the 1884 Toledo Association team.
2. The real name of Pete Gray.
3. The somewhat apocryphal Giant good-luck charm in the early teens.
4. He so impressed the Senators in the '20s while a convict that they worked hard to have him released early from prison. Unfortunately he failed to impress once he hit the street and never played a single game in the majors.

5. Promising Card rookie who lost an eye to Jim Dickey's batting-practice liner in spring training in 1951. He tried long and hard to make it with only one lamp but never quite succeeded. Strangely, Dickey, who looked like a real comer in his own right, never made it either.

6. The only one-legger ever to play in the majors. He made it as a hurler for one game with the 1945 Senators.

7. The Al Schacht of the '40s. Like Schacht, and unlike Max Patkin, another clown of that era, he actually played a few games in the majors—with the 1946 Indians.

8. Campanella's counterpart, he was the AL's first black catcher, arriving from the Negro leagues at the advanced age of 40.

9. The real name of Rube Schauer, who, along with Ferd Schupp, formed the infamous "Hall Room Boys" duo that was the despair of McGraw in the mid-teens.

10. Prior to Don Grate, he held the record for the longest baseball throw for many years.

11. The last big-topper to lose 30 games in a season in 1899.

12. He was the unlucky man on the mound for the Tigers when Eddie Gaedel, all 3'7" of him, strolled up to the plate for the Browns in 1951.

5TH INNING
Monickers

1. Tully Hartsel. **2.** Walter Christensen. **3.** Frank Crespi. **4.** Sylvester Donnelly. **5.** Tony Mullane. **6.** Emil Verban. **7.** Jim Galvin. **8.** Dick Stuart. **9.** Tony Lazzeri. **10.** Mack Jones. **11.** Pompeyo Davalillo. **12.** Charlie Pabor, the old National Association star. **13.** Louis Berger. **14.** Herman Clifton.

6TH INNING
Ole Man River

1. Ulysses Simpson Grant McGlynn. **2.** Heinie Meine. **3.** Connie Johnson. **4.** Oscar Judd. **5.** Estel Crabtree. **6.** Bob Thurman and George Crowe. **7.** Orie Arntzen. **8.** Spud Chandler. **9.** George Bell. **10.** Joe Hatten. **11.** Joe Berry. **12.** Mickey Haeffner. **13.** Alex McColl. **14.** Wild Bill Hutchinson. **15.** Dick Newsome.

One-Year Wonder

1. Henry Schmidt. **2.** Irv Waldron. **3.** Hector Rodriguez.
4. Harry Moore. **5.** Bob Maier. **6.** Eddie Yuhas. **7.** Buzz
Arlett. **8.** Tony Bartirome. **9.** Jim Barbieri. **10.** Herman
Reich. **11.** Cy Buker. **12.** Johnny Sturm.

8TH INNING
The Unrewarded

1. Carl Reynolds. **2.** Minnie Minoso. **3.** Dale Mitchell.
4. Gus Mancuso. **5.** Jimmy Ryan. **6.** Hal Trosky.
7. Johnny Moore. **8.** Enos Slaughter. **9.** Fred Tenney.
10. Mike Tiernan. **11.** Gus Triandos. **12.** Wes and Rick
Ferrell.

9TH INNING
Bonus Busts

1. Joe Tepsic. **2.** Billy Joe Davidson. **3.** Kenny Kuhn.
4. Tom Carroll. **5.** Billy Consolo. **6.** Reno Bertoia.
7. Joey Amalfitano. **8.** Bob Garibaldi. **9.** Gus Keriazakos.
10. Charlie Bicknell. **11.** Frank Leja. **12.** Jim Small.

Game 4

1ST INNING
Hall of Fame Hokum

1. Tommy McCarthy. **2.** Billy Herman. **3.** Sam Crawford.
4. Harry Hooper. **5.** Pete Browning. **6.** Dave Orr. **7.** Early
Wynn. **8.** George Davis. **9.** Chick Hafey and Joe
Medwick. **10.** Sam Rice. **11.** Vic Willis. **12.** George Van
Haltren. **13.** Arky Vaughan. **14.** Chuck Klein. **15.** Rabbit
Maranville, .258. **16.** Jack Powell.

2ND INNING
It's All Relative

1. Mort Cooper and Bobbie Shantz. **2.** Ewart "Dixie"
Walker, and sons, Dixie and Harry. **3.** The Sadowskis,
Bob, Ted, and Eddie. The fourth Sadowski, also named
Bob, was not part of the family. **4.** The Gilberts—Larry,
and sons, Charlie and Tookie. **5.** Carlyle. **6.** Bill and
George Dickey. **7.** Johnny and Chris Van Cuyk. **8.** Alex

and Ron Johnson. **9.** Eddie and Joe Erautt. **10.** Mayer ...
Erskine and Sam: real names, James and Samuel
Erskine. **11.** Herman and Duane Pillette.

3RD INNING
Outstanding Offenders

1. Topsy Hartsel. **2.** Jerry Lynch. **3.** Lawrence "Hack"
Miller. **4.** Clyde Milan, 88 thefts in 1912. **5.** Norman
Cash. **6.** Ted Williams, 40 in 1958. **7.** Hal Chase, the NL
leader in 1916. **8.** Mantle (Reiser didn't begin to switch-
hit until late in his career). **9.** Eddie Collins, 1299;
Tommy Corcoran, 1135; Sam Rice, 1078; Charlie
Grimm, 1078; Jimmy Ryan, 1073; Jimmy Dykes, 1071;
Willie Davis, 1051; Joe Judge, 1034; Fred Clarke, 1015.
10. Ross Barnes. **11.** Larry Doyle, .320 in 1915. **12.** Ned
Williamson. Prior to 1884 all balls hit out of the Chicago
park were ground-ruled doubles. For that one year they
counted as homers. **13.** Sam Crawford and KiKi Cuyler.

4TH INNING
Unlikely Hero

1. Freddie Martin. **2.** Earl Webb. **3.** Duster Mails. **4.** Fred
Whitfield. **5.** Beau Bell. **6.** Felix Mantilla. **7.** Bob Cerv.
8. Billy Moran. **9.** Charlie Neal. **10.** Louie Aloma.
11. Ron Necciai. **12.** Don Padgett. **13.** Chicken Wolf.

5TH INNING
All-Star

1. Arky Vaughan. **2.** Red Schoendienst. **3.** Lefty Gomez.
4. Al Benton. **5.** 1973. **6.** Catfish Hunter. **7.** Vida Blue.
8. Frank Robinson. **9.** Newcombe, Robinson,
Campanella, and Doby. **10.** Frankie Frisch.

6TH INNING
Walking Wounded

1. Hal Peck. **2.** Lou Brissie. **3.** Creepy Crespi. **4.** Jack
Hamilton. **5.** Eddie Waitkus. **6.** Tony Horton. **7.** Max
Alvis. **8.** Larry and Dick Brown. **9.** Herb Score.
10. Charlie Gelbert. **11.** Phil Marchildon. **12.** Cass
Michaels. **13.** Jonathon Stone.

7TH INNING
Hose

1. Mungo ... who else? **2.** Ned Garver. **3.** Noodles Hahn, with the 1901 Reds. **4.** Tom Seaton. **5.** Curt Simmons. **6.** Jack Taylor. **7.** Johnny Antonelli and Joey Jay. **8.** 29, Newhouser, 1944. **9.** Howard Ehmke. **10.** Gus Weyhing. **11.** Jouett Meekin. **12.** Bob Feller and Early Wynn. **13.** Jack Pfiester, 1.15; Carl Lundgren, 1.17; Three Finger Brown, 1.39; and Eddie Reulbach, 1.69. Needless to say, the Cubs' staff that year set a record low of 1.73. **14.** Win Mercer.

8TH INNING
The Ignoble and the Ignominious

1. Denny Galehouse. **2.** Jimmy O'Connell. **3.** Hal Chase. **4.** Hubert "Dutch" Leonard. **5.** Skeeter Shelton. **6.** Jim Devlin, George Hall, Bill Craver and Al Nichols. **7.** Ralph Schwamb. **8.** Dee Fondy. **9.** Pedro Ramos. **10.** Bingo Binks. **11.** Harry Eisenstat. **12.** The seventh game of the 1912 Series; Fred Snodgrass was the goat, having dropped a liner right at him prior to Merkle's miscue. **13.** Al Worthington. **14.** Jim Northrup and Curt Flood.

9TH INNING
Jack of all Trades

1. Cy Seymour. **2.** Cesar Tovar. **3.** Granny Hamner. **4.** Dick Hall. **5.** Jack Bentley. **6.** Second; third. **7.** Dave Foutz. **8.** Ben Chapman. **9.** Woodie Held. **10.** Jack Harshman. **11.** Erv Dusak. **12.** Bill Earle. **13.** Red Lucas. **14.** Johnny Cooney.

Game 5

1ST INNING
Wine for Water

1. Heinie Zimmerman and Frankie Frisch. **2.** Roy Smalley. **3.** Joe Gordon. **4.** Bill Wambsganss. **5.** Pete Rose. **6.** Bob Elliott. **7.** Red Stallcup. **8.** Don Blasingame. **9.** Sollie Hemus. **10.** George Kelly. **11.** Rip Collins. **12.** Joe Sewell.

2ND INNING
Monickers

1. Lou Novikoff. **2.** Dick Porter. **3.** Frank Schulte.
4. Albert Selbach. **5.** George Tebeau. **6.** George Shuba or
Mike Chartak. **7.** Pete Browning. **8.** Sam McDowell.
9. Bob Roth. **10.** Sammy Strang. **11.** Edmund Lopat.
12. Gus Zernial. **13.** Charles McFarland. **14.** Clarence
Childs.

3RD INNING
Expansion Esoterica

1. Gene Brabender, with Seattle. **2.** The 1962 Angels
played .536 ball and finished third, their highest finish
ever. **3.** Dick Donovan, with the Senators. **4.** Gene
Woodling. **5.** Harry Craft. **6.** The Angels played .435 ball.
7. Roger Craig. **8.** Alex Johnson, with the 1970 Angels.
9. Frank Howard. **10.** Joe Morgan led the NL in bases on
balls received as a rookie with the 1965 Astros.

4TH INNING
A Man for Another Season

1. Steve Filipowicz. **2.** Greasy Neale. **3.** Paul Giel.
4. Jake Gibbs. **5.** Frankie Baumholtz. **6.** Joe Corbett and
the immortal ... Gentleman Jim. **7.** Paddie Driscoll.
8. Johnny Herrnstein. **9.** Art "The Great" Shires.
10. Dean Look. **11.** Fred Taylor. **12.** Bill Carrigan.

5TH INNING
Not with a Whimper but with a Bang

1. Sandy Koufax. **2.** Joe Gedeon. **3.** Doc Gessler. **4.** Curt
Walker. **5.** Ed Doheny. **6.** Red Donahue. **7.** Bunk
Congalton. **8.** John Ewing, brother of Buck. **9.** Bill
Lamar. **10.** Buck Weaver. **11.** John Cronin. **12.** Vin
Campbell. **13.** Rebel Oakes. **14.** Wilbert Robinson.

6TH INNING
The Ignoble and the Ignominious

1. Danny Moeller, in 1913. **2.** Jack Schappert. **3.** 1968
Tigers; Ray Oyler and Tom Matchick. **4.** Bill Holbert.
5. Wes Covington. **6.** Tom Oliver. **7.** Lonnie Frey.
8. George McBride. **9.** Cliff Curtis; he lost 23 games in
a row for the 1910—11 Braves. **10.** Bill Bergen. **11.** Ike

Pearson. **12.** Ben Cantwell. **13.** Bill Dailey. **14.** Dave Nicholson.

7TH INNING
One-Year Wonder

1. Buddy Blair. **2.** Kitty Brashear. **3.** Ernie Sulik. **4.** Tex Vache. **5.** Ken Hunt. **6.** Jocko Flynn. **7.** Jim Baxes. **8.** Art Mahan. **9.** Carlos Bernier. **10.** Troy Herriage. **11.** Curt Raydon. **12.** John Paciorek.

8TH INNING
Hose

1. Clarence Mitchell. **2.** Harry Coveleskie. **3.** Johnny Broaca. **4.** Eddie Watt. **5.** Wilbur Wood, Hoyt Wilhelm and Bob Locker. **6.** Jim Hardin. **7.** Dutch Levsen, in 1926 with Cleveland. **8.** Cal McLish. **9.** Jim Konstanty; he started the 1950 Series opener for the Phils. **10.** Ken Brett. **11.** Hal Newhouser. **12.** Early Wynn. **13.** Irving "Young Cy" Young, for the 1905 Braves.

9TH INNING
Team Teasers

1. The 1927 A's had Cobb, Simmons, Cochrane, Wheat, Grove, Foxx and Eddie Collins on their active roster and yet finished 19 games behind the Yankees.
2. Delahanty, Hamilton and Sam Thompson. The super sub was Tuck Turner.
3. The 1908 Indians.
4. Don Lang, 1948; Eddie Kazak, 1949; Tommy Glaviano, 1950; Billy Johnson, 1951. Kazak was the All-Star but was injured prior to the game and couldn't play.
5. The Giants and Pirates, in that order.
6. The Tigers; the draftee of course was Dick Wakefield.
7. Vern Bickford won 11 and Bill Voiselle won 13.
8. No, but the 1967 Red Sox won after finishing ½ game out of the basement the previous year.
9. Mossi, Narleski and did you forget ... Hal Newhouser?
10. The 1930 Phillies.
11. Mickey Livingston, Dewey Williams and Paul Gillespie. The pre-War regular was Clyde McCullough.
12. The Indians.
13. In 1915 the Phils won and the Giants were last.

Game 6

The Unrewarded

1. Rip Radcliff. 2. Cy Williams. 3. Johnny Allen. 4. John Picus Quinn. 5. Emil "Dutch" Leonard. 6. Ethan Allen. 7. Wally Schang. 8. George Burns. 9. Eddie Konetchy. 10. Larry Jackson.

2ND INNING
Don't Fence Me In

1. Roy Cullenbine, Rudy York and Jeff Heath. 2. Chuck Klein, in 1932. 3. Gus Zernial and Braggo Roth. 4. Joe Hauser. 5. Leon Wagner, 28; Ken Hunt, 25; Lee Thomas, 24; Earl Averill, 21; and Steve Bilko, 20. 6. Jim Gentile, 46; Harmon Killebrew, 46; Rocky Colavito, 45; and Norm Cash, 41. 7. Ed Delahanty, July 15, 1896. 8. Hugh Duffy, 18; Lowe, 17; Jimmy Bannon, 13; Tommy McCarthy, 13; and Herman Long, 12. 9. Billy Williams and Stan Musial.

3RD INNING
Rookie

1. Jimmy Nealon. 2. Cuckoo Christensen. 3. Bob Chesnes. 4. Larry Cheney. 5. John O'Rourke, Orator's younger brother. 6. Vean Gregg. 7. Oscar Jones. 8. Dick Drott. 9. Lee Thomas. 10. Hughie Critz. 11. Gavvy Cravath. 12. Chuck Estrada. 13. Toby Atwell. 14. Billy Klaus. 15. Lou Klein.

4TH INNING
Yankee Caddies

1. Sammy Byrd. 2. Jack Reed. 3. Art Jorgens. 4. Roy Sherid; rough one, huh? 5. Charlie Silvera. 6. Jack Saltzgaver. 7. Don Heffner. 8. Jim Brideweser. 9. Ross Moschitto. 10. Joe Glenn.

5TH INNING
What Was His Real First Name?

1. Carvel. 2. Elwin. 3. Lynwood. 4. Norman. 5. Nope, not Orestes; it's Saturnino. 6. Truett. 7. Sylvester. 8. James.

9. Alfonso. **10.** Daniel ... 'ja get it? **11.** Edmundo. **12.**
Charles. **13.** Hazen. **14.** Lewis. **15.** Horace. **16.** George.
17. Maurice. **18.** Cecil. **19.** Michael. **20.** Oscar. **21.** Omar.
22. William. **23.** DeWitt. **24.** Charles. **25.** Herman.

6TH INNING
Ole Man River

1. Roy Schalk. **2.** Guy Curtright. **3.** Kiddo Davis.
4. Jimmy Austin. **5.** George Zuverink. **6.** Marv Grissom.
7. Danny Taylor. **8.** Eddie Mayo. **9.** Birdie Tebbetts.
10. Lou Johnson. **11.** Jake Weimer. **12.** George
McConnell. **13.** Don Johnson. **14.** Joe Boley. **15.** Urbane
Pickering.

7TH INNING
Who'd They Come Up With?

1. Astros. **2.** Athletics. **3.** Orioles. **4.** Red Sox. **5.** Giants.
6. Orioles. **7.** Yankees. **8.** Browns. **9.** Browns. **10.** White
Sox. Did you foolishly say the Giants? **11.** White Sox.
12. Reds. **13.** Cubs. **14.** Yankees. **15.** Yankees. **16.** Tigers.
17. Cubs. **18.** Reds. **19.** Indians. **20.** Tigers. **21.** Dodgers.

8TH INNING
Jack of All Trades

1. Dode Criss. **2.** Chico Salmon. **3.** Harmon Kiilebrew.
4. Mike Ryba. **5.** Willie Smith. **6.** Bobby Bragan.
7. Jimmy Johnston. **8.** Russ Wrightstone.

9TH INNING
The Changing Game

1. 1931. **2.** 1908. **3.** 1929. **4.** 1950. **5.** Would you believe
1976? For many years, before the '70s, the answer was
1929. **6.** 1894 ... a pivotal year in many ways. **7.** 1957.
8. His ERA exactly matched that of the entire National
League in 1930, the worst season modern pitchers have
ever suffered.

Game 7

1ST INNING
Not with a Whimper but with a Bang
1. Norm McMillan. **2.** Culley Rikard. One of the great

baseball names but how long's it been since you heard it? **3.** Joe Adcock. **4.** Baby Twombley. What? You got it? I don't believe it! **5.** Johnny Hodapp. **6.** Hank O'Day. **7.** Dick Brodowski. **8.** Pink May. **9.** Bid McPhee. **10.** Max Butcher. **11.** Tilly Shafer. **12.** Bill "Wagon Tongue" Keister. **13.** Oris Hockett.

2ND INNING
Rookie

1. Rico Carty. **2.** Roy Foster. **3.** Topper Rigney. **4.** Duane Kuiper. **5.** Chuck Schilling. **6.** Earl Sheely. **7.** Tom Tresh. **8.** Smead Jolley. **9.** Manny Jiminez. **10.** Roy Patterson. **11.** Dick Cox. **12.** Pete Ward. **13.** Rich Rollins. **14.** Sonny Jackson. **15.** Don Bessent.

3RD INNING
Team Teasers

1. Louisville. **2.** Washington. **3.** Chicago, St. Louis, Hartford, Boston, Louisville, New York, Philadelphia and Cincinnati. **4.** The 1968 Tigers with a regular cast of Cash, .263; McAuliffe, .249; Wert, .200; and Oyler, .135. The two top subs, Matchick and Tracewski, hit .203 and .156 respectively. **5.** The 1969 Mets. Jones and Agee were the only two to bat over 400 times; Garrett, as a utility man, got in exactly 400 at-bats. **6.** The Yanks were Henrich, Di Mag and Billy Johnson. For the Sox, Williams, Doerr, and I'll bet you forgot Jake Jones. **7.** The 1944 Tigers. Newhouser won 29 and Trout won 27. **8.** Dead last, of course. **9.** The White Sox; Minoso had 31 steals and Busby 26. **10.** The 1958 Braves and the 1968 Tigers. **11.** Our friends the White Sox again. In 1910. **12.** The 1963–64 Orioles. **13.** The Indians. **14.** Yep, the White Sox again. **15.** The 1925–30 Red Sox.

4TH INNING
Unlikely Hero

1. Jimmy Viox. **2.** Jim Palmer, Dave McNally and Wally Bunker. **3.** Bob Purkey. **4.** Bo Belinsky. **5.** Sam Dente. **6.** Willard Marshall. **7.** Tim Jordan. **8.** Julian Javier. **9.** Elmer Riddle. **10.** Flint Rhem. **11.** Phil Regan. **12.** Dick Hyde. **13.** Chuck Essegian. **14.** Phil Paine. **15.** Jack Dalton.

5TH INNING
Hose

1. Ken Holtzman. 2. Harry Brecheen. 3. Jim Bagby, in 1920. 4. Bob Feller, 36 games in 1946. 5. Johnny Wyatt. 6. Nolan Ryan, 5.26 hits in 1972; second, oddly enough, is Luis Tiant, who allowed only 5.30 hits in 1968. So much for the superiority of old-timers. 7. Waddell, Feller, Johnson, Koufax, Ryan, Carlton, McDowell, Blue and Lolich. 8. Johnny Wyatt ... once again. 81 in 1964. 9. Firpo Marberry. 10. Chuck Stobbs. 11. Eddie Rommel. 12. Dom McMahon and Ron Perranoski. 13. Warren Spahn and Ted Lyons.

6TH INNING
Managerial Meanderings

1. George and Dick Sisler. 2. Burt Shotton. 3. Kid Gleason. 4. Mickey Cochrane. 5. Hughie Jennings and Ralph Houk. Houk may one day win another, but don't hold your breath waiting on it to happen. 6. Bill McKechnie. 7. Jimmy Dykes. 8. They were the last two to manage in street clothes. 9. Larry Shepard. 10. Eddie Sawyer, in 1950. 11. Mayo Smith. 12. Fred Haney. 13. 1952; Eddie Stanky and Phil Cavaretta. 14. Vedie Himsl, Harry Craft, El Tappe and Lou Klein.

7TH INNING
Outstanding Offenders

1. Snuffy Stirnweiss, .476 in 1945. 2. Don Hoak. 3. Dom DiMaggio. 4. Hank Majeski. 5. Pete Reiser. 6. Eddie Yost, 151 in 1956. 7. Harmon Killebrew, with the 1963 Twins. 8. Paul Hines, in 1878. 9. Nap Lajoie, in 1901. 10. Who else but Ty Cobb, in 1909? 11. Ted Williams, in 1948. 12. Bob Nieman. 13. Peanuts Lowrey and Joe Frazier. 14. Ray Jablonski ... and if you got this one, I'll shake your hand if and when we meet.

8TH INNING
A Man for Another Season

1. Gene Conley. 2. Cliff Aberson. 3. Lloyd Merriman. 4. Gary Roggenburk. 5. Dick Groat. 6. Frank Howard. 7. Ted Kluzewski. 8. The O'Briens. 9. Joe Sparma.

10. Dick Ricketts. **11.** Galen Cisco. **12.** Cotton Nash. **13.** Carl Bouldin. **14.** Johnny Berardino, the main man on "General Hospital."

9TH INNING
Fall Classic

1. Christy Mathewson. **2.** Bevens' near no-hitter; Lavagetto's double breaking up Bevens' stab at a no-hitter; and Gionfriddo's sensational catch of DiMaggio's almost certain homer. **3.** Harry Walker. **4.** 1918. **5.** Lou Boudreau. **6.** 1944. **7.** Doc and Jimmy Johnston, in 1920. **8.** The Phillies. **9.** Jim Thorpe. **10.** For shame if you guessed Ruth and stumbled on this, your last, at-bat. The answer is none other than Smokey Joe Wood.

Performance Tables

Happy with yourself? Resting on your laurels? Before you get too comfortable, maybe you ought to take a look at just how well you did by comparing your overall performance against that of some of the game's stars, both past and present. Over the course of the World Series of Baseball Memorabilia you compiled 824 at-bats; simple arithmetic tells you you needed at least 248 hits to average .300 or better. Similarly, you needed a minimum of 412 points or total bases to earn a .500 slugging percentage. Anything above either of those marks and you start treading on superstar turf.

Before using the tables below to see how you stand, compute your bonus points. Each bonus point is worth two extra hits and four extra total bases. Ideally, when you've got your final totals, you'll find you've hit with the craft of a Cobb and the power of a Ruth.

Batting Average

302 hits = .367 — Ty Cobb
295 hits = .358 — Rogers Hornsby
284 hits = .346 — Ed Delahanty
279 hits = .339 — Nap Lajoie
273 hits = .331 — Stan Musial
267 hits = .324 — Joe Medwick
261 hits = .317 — Roberto Clemente
256 hits = .311 — Jackie Robinson
252 hits = .306 — George Kell
248 hits = .300 — Enos Slaughter

Slugging Average

568 total bases = .690 — Babe Ruth
522 total bases = .634 — Ted Williams
502 total bases = .609 — Jimmy Foxx
475 total bases = .579 — Joe DiMaggio
460 total bases = .559 — Hank Aaron
451 total bases = .548 — Ralph Kiner
438 total bases = .533 — Mel Ott
427 total bases = .520 — Harry Heilmann
418 total bases = .509 — Harmon Killebrew
412 total bases = .500 — Ernie Banks